IRON ON MY MIND

Go Ph

We press on

dave draper

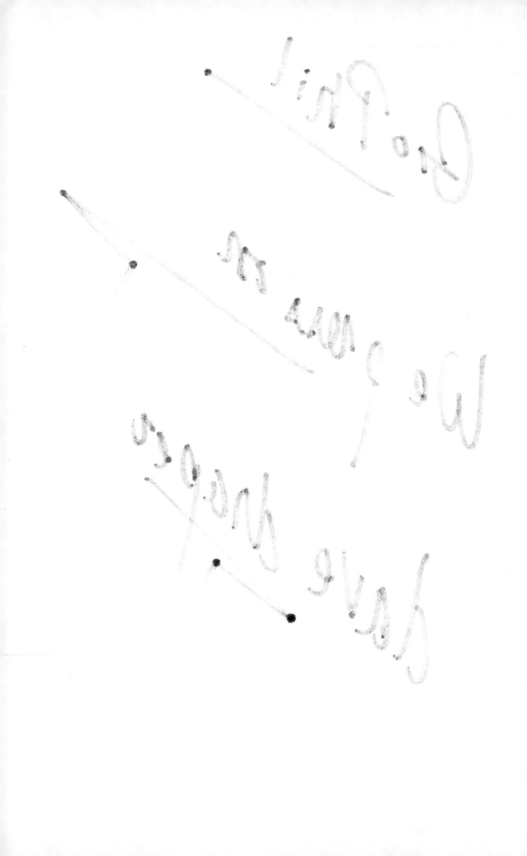

IRON ON MY MIND

Dave Draper

Quotes
Dave Draper

Foreword
Dick Tyler

Imagework
Laree Draper

On Target Publications
Santa Cruz, California

Iron On My Mind

Dave Draper

Quotes: Dave Draper

Imagework: Laree Draper

Foreword: Dick Tyler

Copyright © 2006, Dave Draper
ISBN-10: 1-931046-77-8 — ISBN-13: 978-1-931046-77-0

On Target Publications
P. O. Box 1335
Aptos, CA 95001 USA
(888) 466-9185
info@ontargetpublications.com
www.ontargetpublications.com

Library of Congress Cataloging-in-Publication Data
Draper, Dave.
  Iron on my mind : thoughts on muscle building from the blond bomber / Dave Draper ; imagework Laree Draper ; foreword Dick Tyler.
    p. cm.
  ISBN-13: 978-1-931046-77-0 (pbk.)
  ISBN-10: 1-931046-77-8 (pbk.)
  1. Bodybuilding. 2. Bodybuilders--United States--Biography. I. Title.
  GV546.5.D734 2006
  613.7'13--dc22
                        2005028825

Contents

Preface 7

Foreword 11

Yesterday, Today and Tomorrow 15

The Farmer Bomber 21

Muscularity in 2,100 Words 27

A Word to the Choir 35

Another Week Older and Deeper in Debt 39

Barbells and Muscles and Those in Pursuit 43

The First Cut is the Deepest 49

Spare the Rod, Spoil the Ironhead 53

The Exceptions Rule 59

The Decline 63

The Indoctrination of a Bomber 67

Training Motivators 73

Another Month 81

Aren't You Glad You're a Bomber? 87

Away from the Maddening Crowd 91

Lack of Motivation 99

Barrels, Anvils and Logs 107

Training Motivation, Intensity 113

Bomb Squad Discourse 121

Breaking the Mold 127

Down the Highway and on My Mind 131

Eat, Train and Be Happy 137

Welcome Time and He Loosens His Grip 141

Training Attitude: Sunshine on a Rainy Day 147

Lighten Up and Fly Right 151

Just Another Day 155

Just Another Year 161

Monday, Monday. Two More Reasons to Lift Weights 167

Confusion Brings Clarity Where None Exists 173

Much to Say About Nothing 181

Attitude Awareness, Adjustment and Finesse 187

The Contest: To Enter or Not to Enter 193

Obesity and the Emotions 197

Contents — *Continued*

Perfect, More Perfect, Most Perfect 201
Personal Safety, National Security 207
Take a Walk on the Wild Side 211
Prevention's Sweeter than the Cure 217
Ready or Not Here I Come 221
Rumbling and Rambling, Raving and Roving 225
Some Things Never Change 233
Song of the Whooping Crane 237
Dungeon Duty 243
Sunrise Over Bomber Field 251
Tell It to the Tooth Fairy 259
The Big Chill 265
What If? Never! 273
The Supermarket Connection 277
Solid Nutrition, Bold Workouts, Muscular Body 283
To Soar Like Eagles 289
Why We Do What We Do 295
Train With Confidence 303
True Adventures Presents: Obesity in America 307
Twist of Lemon 313
Mighty Muscles, Brawny Character 319
Peaks and Valleys and Plateaus 327
Got a Sec? Have a Question. 333
When in Doubt, Ramble On 337
Bring on the Pool, Hot Tub and Dancing Girls 345
Torn Quads and Growing Waistlines Unite 349
You Lift, You Learn, You Grow 355
You Win, You Lose, You Crawl 359
Thorns and Roses 365
Afterword — Behind the Smile 373

Preface

In December of 1998 my wife, Laree, thumbed through the pages of *Websites for Dummies* and by February of '99 we had our very own. We were — how do you say it? — on the cutting edge.

We stared at our three-page internet contribution in awe and proudly exclaimed, "We're out there; we're in cyberspace." Now what? I yawned; she shrugged her shoulders. So much for cheap thrills.

By the end of the first week floating around in un-chartered territory, we received thirty-seven email messages. What's this? A few friends and acquaintances announced their approval, thank you, but who were these folks from Oklahoma, New Mexico and New Delhi? One young guy from Indiana cried out that he'd been training for over five years and still couldn't get a peak on his biceps. He was desperate, "What should I do?" Other emails probed dietary issues, overtraining, aging and training methodology and some offered thanks and encouragement.

The silent, static and spare web pages stirred with life.

"I've been following you since I saw you on the cover of a muscle magazine in the mid-'60s. Keep up the good work," signed, Louie from Hoboken.

"Me? Following me? Gee!"

"How do I bulk up? Arnold, Zane and you are the best! How do I trim down? I miss the good old days! How do I get huge and ripped?"

The email kept coming in, from New Zealand to Uzbekistan, Maine to Peru.

I responded to the notes directly and answered questions when asked. "How considerate," I thought, "of this small loyal group to write."

Before the second week had gone by, Laree counted 125 messages from strangers saying hi and looking for help. We decided to glean through the stack and present the most informative and motivating Q 'n' As online for all to share. Very popular.

Week by week the mail grew, the page content expanded and the website evolved, as healthy living things do when under structural pressure. A free weekly newsletter called *Draper Here* became the solution to the ever-increasing, ever-fascinating email load. It's been going out for seven years to everyone who requests it and we haven't missed an issue yet.

The subject matter ranges from sets and reps of exercises to build muscle and might, to the complex yet simple process of aging. What does one do if he or she has never before entered a gym or performed fitness exercise and what does one do the last weeks before bodybuilding competition to exhibit maximum muscle size and definition? The theme of the newsletters is encouragement — to train hard, consistently and positively and to eat smartly; the rewards are extraordinary and the price is right. Be consistent, stick to the basics and there are no secrets.

Iron On My Mind is a collection of sixty-two newsletters from the 350 published over the years. Each chapter is a trip of its own. And throughout the book what I call blasts, bombardments of info, energy, caution and reprimand, are periodically inserted to affirm your purpose, aright your direction and challenge your performance. There is no theme, the articles follow no order. They can be ingested randomly when the spirit moves you, like a shot of wonder protein before a workout. Sip or slug, I hope they satisfy and you never grow full.

Who's the Bomber, you ask? The bomber is the guy who flies the craft at the head of the fleet. You do fly, don't you? No problem; you'll learn.

Dave Draper
Santa Cruz, California

Foreword

I had been a writer of sorts long before I started working for Joe Weider. When I began working at the warehouse, my job was to go to health food stores and try to place Weider products in them.

It soon became evident from my less-than-impressive sales reports, yet grand tales of the stores and store owners, that I was a far better writer than a saleman, so write I did.

Many an hour was spent in the storeroom typing stories about and for the leading bodybuilders of the time. With the exception of such greats as Mozee, Wayne, Tanny and Liederman, bodybuilders were not expected to write. Their job description was to train, train and train some more. Some of the brightest people I've known have been bodybuilders, but writing takes a certain type of creative mind. You have to take the twenty-six letters of the alphabet and arrange them in such a way that the reader will find the words formed interesting and, if possible, inspiring.

Now in the storeroom, where I so ardently tried to create verbal works of art, was a blond giant who used his great power to lift and move heavy boxes around the office. His name was Dave Draper and while he had every reason to express conceit about his physique and strength, he never did. In fact he was, and is, one of the most humble people I've ever known.

During breaks he would sit quietly devouring cans of tuna fish and talking softly. You'd have to work sometimes to draw him into a conversation. If you worked at it long enough, you were rewarded with magnificent stories laced with training wisdom and humor. He became a wonderful friend and is to this day. In spite of his modesty, or maybe because of it, for years his literary talents lay dormant.

It wasn't until recently when I began receiving the Draper online newsletters that I realized the greatness of his unique writing style. Column after column flooded my computer. Those essays were filled with humor and all the training nuances of a bodybuilding icon. We were being taught with such literary grace we never felt we were in a classroom — rather that we were in the gym with him sitting on a bench next to ours. The stories were rich with personal anecdotes and information that could be used in our next workouts.

Now, at last, Dave has come to realize the practical and historical importance of his work and has taken many of his columns and put them into book form. I cannot express strongly enough what a treasure this is.

Only those who love bodybuilding, however, need apply for this volume. It must be read and used as long as you cherish the clanging of plates and the sweet smell of sweat from a good workout. As long as you crave muscle mass and great strength and as long as you want both a healthy mind and body you will need this book.

To my list of the four greatest bodybuilding authors I've added one more.

Dick Tyler
Rocklin, California

Yesterday, Today and Tomorrow

I remember when I was kid working out in my corner of a bedroom shared with two older brothers. I can recall only bits and pieces of my pre-teen iron struggles, causing me to wonder how much I trained at all. Ah, but these patchy images disclose that the novelty of exercise was outlived and replaced by enduring hard labor instead. I approached my meager thirty-minute bouts with the iron less like play and more like self-imposed detention from which I needed release. A peculiar pastime for a ten-year-old; how long is this boyhood infatuation going to last?

Evidently, by rummaging through wall charts and mimicking exercises demonstrated by the Brunet brothers — remember them, muscular Canadian twins working for an aspiring Montreal entrepreneur, Joe Weider, circa mid-'50s? — I had devised a routine that was worthy of sufficient repetition to cause severe boredom and — what's this? — some accompanying lumps of muscle. I learned early on this weight lifting stuff was not a game you played like batter-up baseball, jump-and-shoot basketball or pass-and-run football. It was me, myself and I crowded at the end of a lumpy bed with a stack of jangling and defiant weights that no one cared about but me.

My recollections picture me alone as I rolled the wobbly inert mass around the worn linoleum floor. I balanced them on end and crawled under them. I pushed and pulled them, curled and pressed 'em. I mightily applied the bothersome flat alloy wrench to the bright red collar's adjustment screw and changed the weights from light to heavy and back again, always expecting the plates to dislodge and fall on my head. The screws left barbed gouges in the 16-inch bars, good for an occasional cut on the mits.

The object wasn't cheering and scoring points, winning or losing, today, tomorrow or this season. The purpose wasn't skilled running and jumping, throwing and catching and bouncing off a teammate's energy on a sunny field in a vigorous afternoon. The motive was survival, muscle and might and self against self, prompted by wishful thinking and a kid's hope and dream — a daring image of a well-muscled dave-man bopping about in my morsel-sized mind. Where'd that come from? Now you see him, now you don't.

My next cast-iron memory includes a pair of dumbbells and a bar next to a mattress in the corner of the basement, two chairs back-to-back for dips and a splintery wooden chinning bar rigged across overhead beams. I'm 15 and the Weehawken High School coach calls me "Arms" every time he sees me. He's cool. I'm quiet. He allows me to tumble and walk on my hands in the corner of the gym floor — corners suit me fine — while the other kids play basketball during PE.

[Note: "PE," or "phys ed," or "physical education," once part of the public school curriculum, is an obsolete and primitive form of activity, the erroneous focus of which was to condition and entertain children and young adults and instruct them in the absurd need for exercise and sports participation. Forward-thinking educators replaced the frivolous expenditure of time and energy with video-game analysis, cell-phone communications and iPod Studies 101.]

I remember, too, a rare sight in a fancy New England prep school where kids of wealth studied for future enrollment in slick universities. Under my bed was that same barbell I hoisted in the basement in Jersey. It was a curious thing in the dorms of Avon Old Farms, where tennis racquets, jai-alai gear and pictures of home hung on the walls next to the bunks. After studies and before lights-out, I rolled the rude iron hunk from its resting place and put it through some hefty motions. Little clinks and clanks could be heard amid the din of young teens releasing their pent-up evening energies. Rumor had it there wasn't another barbell in all of Connecticut. Drapes is weird.

This less-than-rich scholarship student from Secaucus never saw the inside of a slick university. Jerry, my older brother, was about to graduate Yale when he asked me what school I was going to attend in the fall. I stared at my tuna on whole wheat, shrugged my shoulders and said, "I dunno." He said wisely, "Where there's a will, there's a way." That was the end of that conversation. I got a job, ironically, in a metal fabricating factory and bought a pair of 45-pound plates with my first paycheck. Ask Leroy Colbert, he stashed them in my car.

The sequence of rusty recollections increases and clarifies from here. An adult-like head pops through the bog of dependent youth and I'm on my own to locate and inspect the obstacles of life. I drag the 45s up a flight to my very own one-room apartment, where they join the weights of my childhood at the end of yet another bed. The pile of steel looks impressive and I wonder if the floor to the old flat can sustain the weight. I clean and press 185, a first for me and, no doubt, the creaking boards beneath my feet. We're in there.

Seventeen and I still haven't read a muscle magazine. Who needs them? The wall charts are long gone and I'm propelled forward by the same force that set me in motion a lifetime ago, my imagination. The unseen and determined mover is comfortably settled in the unconscious halls of my mind. The mind plays a critical role in weight lifting and building might, you know. And instincts contribute generously, when you let them. Lifting is something I know personally and privately, a need, a fullfilment, a diversion, a companion, a teacher, a source of power, a motivator and a swell musclebuilder. It makes smooth the rough places. Being strong is fun and enabling, impressive and protective.

Before the foot of the bed, a temple of sorts, in that dismal silent room, I remember doing barbell rows, stiffarm pullovers, overhead pressing and press-behind-necks, light benches, barbell curls, dips and chins and pushups and lunges. They gave the four walls and me life. Three sets of this and that every day for eight to 15 reps seemed to work. Some days I had it, some days I didn't; some things never change. Focus was coming slowly, patience remained at a crawl, discipline was being ground into my skull and resolve led the barking pack. Form needed work and muscle identity and recruitment simply took time and practice — inevitable maturity. Fortitude quite naturally joined my resolve. Call it the evolution of a musclehead that cannot be hastened.

Still, the iron doesn't move without a lot of hard work and sacrifice, discipline and persistence. After a day's work, there it is... the barbell in front of the bed.

On frequent weekends the weights were transported to my vehicle where they lay scattered in noisy confusion till they reached my out-of-town get-away. Lifting on Saturday and Sunday with no time constraints was particularly appealing; I could wallow and test myself in the tranquility of a quaint cabin (leaky shed) in the north. Getting a life had not yet occurred to me.

The weights seemed to follow me wherever I went. Not like a habit or a puppy or body odor, but like an extension of myself, my expression, my need and desire. Some kids sang or danced or sketched or played musical instruments or engaged in sports. Some studied or did nothing in particular or hustled or got into trouble. I lifted weights as if it was my duty, my individual responsibility or private obligation. Unknown to me, lifting was beginning to define who I was.

Then came my first experience with man and weights beyond the limited one-step, two-step lifting in the confines of a bedroom or basement: I joined the YMCA. A raucous group of guys tossed the metal around like it was a bunch of scrap, in a room the size of a closet next to the proverbial boiler room. I learned something about fighting for my turn on the bench and lifting more than the other guy. I learned stuff you need to learn and forget before you learn anything at all. The place was a zoo. Six months in a zoo was enough for this animal and I left in the early fall.

The Vic Tanny's in Jersey City, my next exposure to exercise beyond my innocent view, had red rugs, chrome weights, mirrors on every wall, music and girls. I frowned, looked straight ahead and didn't make a peep. I did my first 400-pound bench press with a chrome training bar and a string of nine chrome 20s and one 10 on each side... don't forget the little chrome collars.

Tanny's was a dog-and-pony show, and I wasn't entertained. It closed down one fine day in late winter and I was off to Weider Barbell's stockroom in Union City. Leroy showed me how to do seated dumbbell alternates; I did my first set of squats and moved to California before the heat of summer.

You might say it was there where I enrolled in my first year of university: UCMB, University of California, Muscle Beach. The year was 1963.

One of these years I'll graduate, go out in the world and get a job. Till then, it's one course after another, day after day, learn, learn, learn and practice, practice, practice. I'm studying for my Master's Degree in Bombing and Blasting.

For some the sky's the limit, for us it's just the start.

The Farmer Bomber

I peeled back the lids of a can of sardines and a can of tuna, plopped the contents on a plate, grabbed a cold bottle of spring water from the fridge and headed for the deck. Heaven on earth. I'd feed the beast and bask in the sun while contemplating the art of amassing time, or aging, as it is commonly referred to in some cultures.

The average person walking the streets — male or female, young or old, your neighborhood or mine — is out of shape, overweight and under-muscled. One could conclude that these physical conditions reflect an under-developed interior as well. How does one miss the magnitude of one's personal health and strength or fail to pursue their maintenance? Something's wrong; the sickness and its symptoms are the same: fat, out of shape, deaf, dumb, blind.

Here's the typical societal scenario — I generalize: When we're young we run around like nuts and our bodies do magic with the stuff we stuff in our mouths and promptly swallow. Time goes by, we slow down and the magic is replaced by a mean trick. Our stomachs expand and our muscles shrink and our nutty energy finds a comfortable place on the sofa to re-cline. We grow old while we're still young and awaken from our long, comfortable snooze to a desperate reality. Age has visited us with all its sordid and deplorable companions. We're a mess.

About us, you and me — specifically, bombers: We're not elite and we're not exclusive, but we are certainly not average or typical. Somewhere along our struggle and play we were struck with our presence and decided to improve ourselves inside and out, and maybe make ourselves the best we can be. We are absolutely on the right track. Weight training, intelligent eating and the avoidance of sloppy and destructive living habits are a wonderful and fulfilling lifestyle to behold. People cross their eyes, stagger backward against a wall, put their hands to their mouths and gasp when invited to join us. Their roots are thinly spread across shallow barren soil. No prosperous harvest for them this season. They are sluggish and lack wisdom. I'm the farmer bomber.

My training, like yours, ranks high on the chart of deeds and interests important to me. It has set the course I travel, or has been, at least, a close and encouraging companion along the way. I reach to gain what it has to give and therefore work out with regularity and intensity. Sessions in the gym are seldom casual, never mechanical and always meaningful. They are at once rugged, rewarding, exhilarating and self-inspired. The point is this: Potentially, all the attributes necessary to proceed forward remain in place, strong and fast, for all of us as we dutifully turn the leaves of the calendar.

There is a caveat in the thought above. Training hard, eating right and building healthy muscle have become priorities over the years of my life — my vocation, pastime, fascination and study. Few folks have the time, desire, purpose and where-with-all to devote to the activity as I. Gauge yourself accordingly.

Another thing, Godzilla. It occurs to me that simply getting in shape and staying in shape are remarkable aspirations and quite enough to fullfil a well-balanced man or woman. And adding some size and ripples and gorilla strength where and when possible is admittedly very cool.

Enough chatter. Let's set some ground rules for the forthcoming conversations: We're all different inside and outside — body, mind and spirit; some are well invested in training and some are relatively new. My points of view are based on my experience, observation and common sense... also guessing, coin tossing, old wives tales, the first thing that comes to my mind, hearsay, astrology, black magic, gossip and rumors. This in no manner places me ahead of you, but gives me the opportunity to identify where you are and suggest how you might move to overcome your wearisome obstacles. With that in mind, let's approach the matters at hand.

What does time hold in store for us? 30 caused me to frown; 40 sneaked by while I engaged in a hazy stupor; 45 found me rebounding like an uncaged jackrabbit; I was building momentum at 50 and at 55 I found myself looking overhead as if waiting for the shoe to drop... there were signs on the trail, swirling clouds on the horizon, voices. I started taking notes.

The ensuing five years followed a course similar to the tortuous Manhattan Express at New York, New York in Las Vegas. I hung on for dear life, being battered around as corkscrews and looptyloops humbled my flesh and bones. The cruise was over and the time had come to pick my way across the uneven and extreme terrain that lay ahead. I became fascinated and renewed my briefly torqued and skewed passion for training. I stopped, I looked and I listened. I spoke. "Time and me. We'll do this together," I said to myself, "one workout at a time."

Did I mention that I am stronger and more capable today than I was five years ago, when I first started hearing voices and talking to myself? I went through a protracted six-month period of wrestling with the demons of aging. What exactly would I be giving up, I wondered? Every old and new pain was a source of amplified doubt and complaining and fear. I shared my grumbling dressed in good humor with my peers at the gym and we had a jolly old time; you know how it goes. We also uncovered a few remedies amid the miseries and swapped war stories. This banter and exchange of ideas served a purpose before becoming as stale as the injuries we lamented. I hate war stories, and conversation on the gym floor I contend should be limited to "Hi" and "How are ya", or "Yo" and "Wassup?" I soon withdrew and resumed my former thoughtful manner and zeroed in on the challenge before me, what to do with the hand I held.

I was on the edge of assuming the conventional response to age and that was entirely too close for comfort. I retreated like a moth before a flame. What's new, what's different that I can't control now that I could before? Truthfully, a long list of things from skin tone and digestion to diminishing muscle size and energy unfolded.

Once recognized, then acknowledged, understood and confronted, you can deal with any age-old problem. Accept, scrutinize and embrace. There. Finally, the secret was revealed: I yielded and ceased fretting over the irritating, fearful limitations of getting older. I grew up and in the transition regained my oversized-kid nature and once again engaged in fixing what appeared unfixable, reforming the mold and providing maximum muscle exertion wherever necessary. I discovered new dimensions of focus, expanded my concentration, eliminated all talking and resumed a deliberate pace. I refreshed workout involvement and redialed commitment, crawled under the squat bar for a new personal record, pulled more than ever before, and gratefully, wisely bid farewell to heavy benches and uncovered profound meaning in light-weight thick-bar bench presses that constructively worked my muscles and spirit.

"Respect thy body and be thankful," I repeated as an admonishment. My joints are mine and have served me well for years and now they hurt. I warmed them up till they glowed, wrapped them and before hungrily grabbing the bar like a roasted turkey leg, placed my hands with deliberate care at the right places and lifted scrupulously. Looked a little dorkey, but the effort's in the nines.

My training today is fundamentally the same as it was when I trained for contests in the '60s and '70s: hard, long, supersetted and volume accented. There's a lesson in this for all of us, new and seasoned, male and female, striving and maintaining. What worked for you in the past will work for you today with appropriate modifications and extraordinary care.

The chief modification beyond emphasizing exercise thoughtfulness, body respect and genuine gratefulness is awareness of overall training load. Blast it, but rest accordingly.

I trained six days a week till I was 50, five days a week till 60 and four days a week since 2004. Observation: The workouts are harder and stronger, more assertive yet slightly slower, less painful and restrictive than in late '90s. Day by day... tomorrow is another chapter.

In the pages ahead I'll address you mature guys and gals with fresh wings who have recently joined the squad. Don't idle on the runway too long; don't waste precious fuel and time and practice. The sky waits for no man or woman.

Muscle, might and mind, what a select combination of qualities to contain in one body. Too often man possesses one characteristic exclusive of the others: He's strong, yet oversized and dull-witted; he's bright, but a physical wreck, or a sturdy fellow without an ounce of understanding.

The three invaluable attributes come together like water, vapor and ice when man works for them with blood, sweat and tears.

Now we have something special, a rare and exclusive blend: strength in all forms at once.

Muscularity in 2,100 Words

I'm thinkin', I'm thinkin'. You should see me. My face is all blotchy and crumpled from the strain. I twitch periodically when a thought is close, otherwise my shoulders are drawn tight by my traps and I'm as rigid as a fire plug. Muscularity for bombers, be they ready or not, that is the subject.

Today's musclebuilding generality: Where you are going and how you get there depend upon who you are and where you are now.

- Where you are going, let's assume, is a well-chosen place of desirable and attainable muscularity.

- Who you are is defined by your history, your genetics and your temperament.

- Where you are now is that place in your journey determined by your acquired lifestyle and habits.

- How you go from place to place is up to us, you and me, with the emphasis on you.

Let's take a look at the most common scenario among you explosive disciples-of-the-skies, consider a course of action and see if we strike a chord or a nerve or my throbbing swollen thumb.

I impose upon you to use your imaginations.

You're a guy of 40-something who worked with weights in a garage with your buddies during high school and got in pretty good shape. Time flies. Job with the city (the firm, school, institute, restaurant, mortuary, maternity ward) and married with two kids had you looking over a gut, 30 extra pounds and diminishing strength and energy. Unacceptable, you join a gym and haven't missed a workout since the grim revelation three years ago. You've lost 20 pounds of fat, gained muscle size, shape and density and you're semi-intentionally holding five to ten pounds of extra mass for strength, workout drive and good luck. It's time to get trim, hard and see what's lurking in the shadows.

You are not alone, a boomer, a product of the golden years of bodybuilding, a Zane, Scott, Howorth, Draper and Arnold knockoff of sorts, having grown up watching us flex in the muscle magazines. You worked out, you fell and now you're back, and, once back, you're back for good. Yes! High-fives all 'round. Now you wanna get ripped.

Be prepared for a few head adjustments. You are required to drop up to ten pounds over the next months to achieve the desired leanness. This is fine on paper and in your imagination, but the actual loss of size in the shoulders and arms is devastating. I revolt; we all revolt. Furthermore, strength diminishes, muscle endurance is compromised and the pump of promise and hope takes a nosedive.

Wait! There's more. You get to eat less scrumptious food and there's no cheating. Swell.

Bulking up is more fun. Can I go home now?

No, you can't. Commitment rules. Reaching for muscle definition can only make you a better person, smarter by experience, tougher by restraint, harder by application, keener by focus and sharper by intensity.

You must keep your eye on the goal. Visualize strong, well-muscled hips, the thickness of the waist replaced by a trim taper and the robust torso minus the layer of thick padding, a clear separation of muscle groups and thin skin that reveals veins and the ripple of underlying muscle — the lean body, active and alive. This is the authentic stuff. Anyone can get big; getting muscular is the real deal. Chumps get fat; champs get muscular. Besides, you can regain your precious monster size practically overnight (eat) if you find yourself sweating, quivering and going through withdrawals. Your choice. Be strong.

If you hear cliché in my presentation, it's in your ear and not in my voice. Listen to what's said and add heart, soul and desire. The truth shall set you free.

You'll need four days in the gym; they will be direct, hard-hitting and concise and neither short nor rushed. Each muscle group needs to be hit twice a week, directly or indirectly. Supersetting will be used generously because it is a most generous method of training. It builds muscle strength, density, tenacity, shape, separation, endurance and energy; it stimulates training focus, involvement and excitement; it creates pace, rhythm and momentum. Supersetting contributes to muscularity like fire contributes to hot. Supersets work.

The heavy weights will be replaced by moderate weights and each exercise executed with meticulous form and intensity. Set, rep and muscle concentration will be taken to advanced degrees of command and responsibility. With lighter, more controllable weight in your grasp, you will demand of the weight, rather than let the weight, oversized and unwieldy, demand of you. A swifter training pace should be sought as you accept your workout modifications and quickly condition yourself to the muscle-defining regimen. I say "quickly" because a new intensity needs to be adopted if you are truly seeking rock-hard muscle and lower bodyfat. The goals before you come at the cost of enthusiastic and exhilarating blasting. Passionate blasting. Blasting and more blasting.

Do not fret. To satisfy your craving for the heavy weights, reserve two workouts a month for your low-rep power onslaught — a great addition and complement to muscularity training. Be smart, be kind and be healthy.

My favorite muscle combinations and workout scheme? Day 1: chest, back and shoulders; 2: biceps and triceps; 3: legs; 4: day off; 5: mix of push 'n' pull according to need and desire; two days off. Sometimes I flip-flop these according to my overtraining barometer or injury scale. Flexible is good.

Short pause for contemplation: Don't you find it interesting — or do you find it boring and dumb? — with the variety of so-called progressive training methodology available, I choose the same old muscle groupings and format? But, they say change is important. I agree. But change can be subtle, according to need and desire and not according to rule, responding to instinct and feel and not because it's the first of the month or the end of a six-week cycle or because it says so in my training log. New and different doesn't always mean progressive and cutting edge. Just thought I'd mention it aloud should you feel the basics and the tried-and-true are stale or old-fashioned and you're missing out on the latest high-tech whatever. The sharp edge is at your fingertips and in your mind.

Nutrition, the foods you eat, the proteins, fats and carbohydrates, the supplements and the extras: Now I get out the yard stick, and not to measure the ingredients, but to bap the butt of the irreverent over-eater and ill-fated consumer of junk. Stand up, step forward and bend over. Smack. How did that feel? Not so good, huh? You may return to your seat and sit, gently. I'll probably hear about my irreverent mistreatment from some abuse activist committee or politically-correct exercise management group policing these pages. I'll be grounded. No more blitzing on weekends and blasting will be confined to aerobic classes only. Require the wicked captain to eat junk food for 30 days. No protein shake. That'll teach him.

Here's the general layout. You've heard it before, and why should it change? Eat more protein, less carbohydrate, ample essential fats and lower your overall consumption; that is, smaller portions here and there in the six meals you'll be consuming throughout the day. You're a bomber, we're all bombers and there'll be no handwringing, counting your calories or balancing your food groups with a calculator. Wing it.

What a dandy group, I might note. Pull up a bench for a sec. We are reasonably seasoned musclebuilders and things of the mind need not concern us. We are not bubbleheads. Disciplines have been established, perseverance exhibited, commitment expressed and evaluations considered. The requirements for each of us seeking rock-hard sinew will be basically the same. All that is necessary are fingers on the tuning dial, hands on the eating, arms around the training and full-body submission to time, finesse, hard work, compromise and patience. It's all under control.

From breakfast to bedtime you'll be eating to serve the body, not your sensory persuasions. There's plenty of delight in the menu of the hard-working weight trainer seeking tight muscles. The food groups are broad, the vital needs are sizeable and we have choices. So ice cream and donuts are not on the list. Smile, there is tuna and water.

Allow me to ramble. Eat less fat than Dr. Atkins suggested. Egg white breakfasts if you fear the yolk (too bad, it's a good fat); trimming the excess fat from meats is not a bad idea. No fried foods or chicken skin and I cringe when I witness lightly cooked bacon entering the human construction zone. Go easy on the carbohydrates (less than the Zone, more than Atkins) and no carbs from dead foods like pasta and potatoes or sugar on the rocks (soda, candy and cakes and booze); limited whole grains like a hardy wheat bread, light on the legumes and beans for now, a few nuts in the palm of your hand is okay. Cut the low-fat milk products in half (cottage cheese, milk, cheese, yogurt) and in half again over time, as it is not uncommon to hear a bodybuilder preparing for a contest say these account for baby fat and thick skin.

Protein builds muscle and supplies energy when in excess. Unless you have a sick liver or kidneys, a large consumption of protein and the variety of amino acids only benefit the body. Think one gram per pound as a minimum and one-and-a-half to two grams per pound as good and greedy. Red meat builds best, fish and poultry trim best, and eggs and dairy are like busy workers scurrying around the construction site picking up stuff, moving and carrying things and keeping order. Now you know my limited vision of nutrition: aminos with hard hats, hormones in boots operating bulldozers, enzymes with their sleeves rolled up reading blueprints spread on the hood of a muddy Dodge Ram.

I repeat. If you are a calorie counter and carefully balance percentages of this and that to achieve physical improvement, stop it, for gosh sakes. Details are good for detectives and researchers and professors, but they distract from the instinctive trusts with which the dynamic musclebuilder forms the mold... or is it, molds the form. See what I mean? That's what calorie counting and other such intellectual preoccupations do. They engross, they mislead, they confuse in the act of perfecting and accurately achieving. They're tiresome and muddle the mind of the aspiring athlete. They bind and they dilute. Now, as I was saying... er... what was I saying?

Living foods are a great source of cellular health and vitality. Eat them regularly; fruits sparingly (high sugar content) and at logical times of the day to serve energy needs and provide ever-loving vitamins, minerals, enzymes and phytonutrients. Yum, taste good, too. The body smiles at their ingestion (more Draper depth). Fresh vegetables lightly cooked and in salads should be eaten in abundance for their carbohydrate, roughage and nutrient value.

We all are different with our individual chemistry, hormones, enzymes, muscle mass, bodyfat and metabolism in tow. I leave it to you to kick around the yams and other carb sources, if you think you need them, and to alter your overall and time-specific quantity intake, as you steer your way through the leaning and learning curves. For example, I require less food intake on off-training days, though eating the same amount provides a mini growth spurt. I eat protein and additional carbs prior to a workout to assure plentiful fuel and nutrient resources. I always feed the beast some carbs and additional protein immediately after the beating is applied, time to replenish, repair and reward the bruised and starving mess. I always eat breakfast, never eat too much at any one serving and each meal is an appropriate combination protein, fat and carbohydrate. When defining I forego the late-night meal and consume a tablespoon of free-form amino acids to satisfy the pre-bedtime protein hit.

A good protein powder and free-form amino acids play an important role in building hard muscle. (You knew that, but you wanted to hear me say it again.) Backing off the food intake requires fortification at the proper times, conveniently and in concentration. I don't disapprove of running the body on low food volume (occasional mini-fast) for cleansing and purging and system relief periodically, especially when leaning down, and provided the limited ingested resources are power-packed. Keep those supplementary vitamins and minerals and antioxidants coming, roughage from Metamucil and lots of water for smooth flying.

God's speed, bombers. And remember, no flying under bridges, no stalling over the White House, stay out of tunnels and no landing on football fields, golf courses, beaches or interstates.

A Word to the Choir

Seeking to lose weight and get fit? Join the ever-growing crowd in both number and girth. Advice and suggestions fall from the sky like drizzle and we are by day's end soaking wet, irritated and confused.

Resolutions come and go like a dotcom business. They're inspired, well intended and often mandatory, yet they lack substance and they lack endurance. Listed among the top ten resolutions is Get in Shape. Everyone resolves to lose those extra pounds, tone the softening muscles and run a mile a day. Within a month, the eager participants either haven't begun or they've given up and life takes on a pale sameness. Digging back in your memory for a moment, where do you stand today?

Getting in shape is a noble prizewinner. If that bold pledge graces your list, your thinking is sound. In my humble opinion from all I've observed from my various perches over a bunch of years, getting in shape and staying in shape attracts more worthy habits and improves one's position in life more than any ten creatively devised resolutions. Get in shape this year and perhaps you won't be pressed to make a list of resolutions for next; by the virtues of this ambitious and audacious year they'll already have been accomplished.

The best way to approach the matter is with a positive mind. Agree? (If you don't we're speaking different languages and are probably from different planets... welcome to Earth.) Don't think of the time, work and discomfort you might endure to become fit. Grumbling and excuses can sink a ship before it sets sail for adventure and discovery: which gym, how much and where, it's across town, I don't have time, I need to lose weight first, I'll go if you go, the kids, the spouse, the dog, and, Oh, my aching back. Stop it. You're giving yourself a headache, and I ain't feeling too good either.

Attitude rules. Think of the everyday ability being lighter, stronger and more toned provides, the relief boundless energy affords and the creative thinking that blossoms from a mind and body not lashed to the stake of diminishing health. It's all there before you. Envision your infancy and the early steps you once took with gleeful trepidation. You goo'd and kicked and rolled over. You struggled as you crawled with great determination to a sturdy object and pulled yourself to a wobbling posture. You let go and were off and never looked back. Well, bright eyes, it isn't any different now. You're just a little older and, we hope, a lot wiser.

We are all different with differing needs. The first step one must take to fully embrace fitness is to recognize its importance. It's a free country and you and I do as we please as the laws allow. However, within us is a world over which we govern, and I believe we are responsible for its well-being. We are obligated to care for ourselves with logic and love. We are in control and can lavish ourselves with exercise and whole-some food and a lovable, sensible lifestyle. What a privilege, friends! You and I are smart, live in abundance and are able to spoil ourselves with good health and internal enthusiasm. Why would we choose or permit anything but the best?

The more cynical bystanders say there are some among the world's communities who are uninformed, lazy and glut-tonous. Ouch. They say mankind eats too much junk food and watches too much TV. Where do they hear these... er... exaggerations... falsehoods... these outright lies? I say, "Time to make a statement here, folks, and apply yourself with re-newed energy to the achievement of your praiseworthy goals: Losing weight and getting in shape."

You can do this.

You start immediately, with resolve, and one step at a time like an innocent and wide-eyed child. When no one else is look-ing, remove all junk foods from the cupboards, countertops and refrigerator. The out-of-sight, out-of-mind principle works. Already you're losing excess fat while vigorously, almost aero-bically, involved in the monumental, energy-consuming clean-up project. Where did all this ooey-gooey stuff come from?

Complete the remaining days of the month with a daily walk and run combination — walk a block, run a block (or some version that is acceptable), walk a block and so on for five, ten or fifteen minutes until the walking is replaced by the run-ning alone. Ease into the subtle and effective plan with cer-tainty, conviction and unselfconscious eagerness. Remember, the rewards far outshine the costs. Keep your eyes focused on the grand purposes and goals, never allowing doubt a wicked foothold.

Choose a regular time each day to practice your running — creating a mindset and daring habit — and follow it immediately with ten minutes of meditative crunches and leg raises.

This simple strategy will introduce you to the thrill and delight of initial muscle soreness (thanks, pal) and familiarize you with the order of the exercise life. You are in training for the more exciting things to come. You will bow to the month on the last day as if it were an old and loyal friend. "Thank you for your patience and good will," you will say as you turn to next month with your head high, shoulders back and gut in — where they belong. You've just begun, mate.

Consider this: Two weeks from today, as you continue in your training, you will be a modestly yet confidently invested fitness devotee. Colors will be brighter, the air sweeter and cumbersome objects more manageable. You can rearrange your furniture whenever you please, carry large bundles and over-sized packages of sharp new clothes purchased during wild spending sprees to fit your sharp new body. The mountains you climb will cast shadows on hills left behind. Stairs will replace elevators, protein will replace sugar and a buoyant self will replace the grim downhearted character too long a companion. You will grasp and expand your training; you will go on to discover that discipline is more than just another ten-letter word. You will press on joyfully toward the continuous renewal of life.

Consider this: What if you don't?

Another Week Older and Deeper in Debt

Another week older and deeper in the year. Repeat after me: I am not selfish and I will not miss my workouts. I am a caring person and I will not miss my workouts. For the sake of others I will enjoy myself and not miss my workouts. I will encourage others and not miss my workouts. I will spread my joy and not miss my workouts. There. Doesn't that make you tingle all over? Sort of like a pumping mantra, a meditative burn. I have a similar incantation that goes like this, "I will not eat like a pig." Very effective when muttered at parties and at the dinner table with family and friends. Try it… or not.

Let's get down to business, shall we? We often circle the sober and pervasive problem of squeezing exercise and well-being into our over-booked, over-looked lives. Are you convinced of the importance of your health, have you taken steps to alter your poor eating habits and are you resolved to setting your puny shoulder to the task of exercise? Are you, quote-unquote, committed? What do you mean you forgot, it slipped your mind, you got busy? Grab the stool, the dunce cap and drag them and your bottom to the corner of the room. Adorn the cap. Have a seat. Think fat, weak and lazy. Do not think muscle, might and spirited. Wasted time is lost time, and we do not have time to lose. Small steps are significant steps, no steps are futility.

Here's what we're gonna do: If you've stalled out completely, we need to re-introduce a scheme of exercise that is not imposing and has regularity. I expect training is not foreign to you but has lost its place of priority due to the circumstances of daily life. You would rather blast it or take nothing at all. Wrong. Nothing-at-all is an infectious disease for which there are not enough antibodies. We need to be in motion and if you are not already, start today. Walk and run splits are a wonderful initiator and motivator. They are done totally to entertain and occupy you for fifteen minutes every other day. Break out your training gear and affectionately stroke your training psyche. Crunches and leg raises on alternate days for fifteen minutes will condition the midsection while athletically extending your workout investment. As you arrange all consequential matters in your life, schedule your training for a particular time every day. Let there be no room for decision. Life's a bully.

Notice your input. Is it perfunctory and lackadaisical? Is your attitude limp and tentative? This is typical of a loser. You must, for our plan to work, gather up genuine internal enthusiasm and apply yourself with confidence and conviction. Void of these life-supporting gems, your efforts will be somewhere near miserable and the returns meager and short-lived. Let the time go by as it may, you are in control and on your way. Sooner or later we can add specific freehand movements to the sufficient foundations. For now, relax and let the momentum build and your unseen plan unfold. You're in action. You're safe.

Your gym, if not in your garage or basement, is across town. The decision, the travel distance, the lockerroom and small talk all take time, time, time. Go twice a week unfailingly (for example, Tuesdays and Thursdays) and eliminate choice. Go to the gym ready for action in your sweats and sneaks (five-minute resourceful change at work) and shower at home. No dull lockerroom snag or loss of impetus. Let your friendly, calm determination be evident on the gym floor as you move to your equipment with assertion and knowing. Dig in and keep moving till the job is done. Give yourself thirty, forty-five or ninety minutes depending on you and the outside world. You're there; perhaps the world will understand, forgive and allow you to live. You are such a better person, after all. Perhaps you can negotiate a Saturday morning or Sunday afternoon workout. Life is good.

My years of crawling around the iron and steel have provided occasion for me to try by accident or curiosity routines of odd proportions — clawed and fanged, one-eyed monsters. These are dart workouts that serve me well, to teach, to perpetuate and yield relief on hard-pressed days. They don't stand alone to build the mass or introduce the novice to the basic truths of weight training.

Live it up and be grateful you have the facility and faculty and freedom. You're born to aspire.

I'm off to the gym — my launching pad — to fly one of these strange contraptions. Stand back. Blast off is scheduled in spite of inclement weather or loose parts.

Our workouts — our training sessions — are not optional. They are as necessary as eating, breathing, sleeping, working and loving. Daily living must include exercise and right eating if we expect to live fully. They are fundamental and essential.

One's relationship with God, one's survival and one's family come first. Exercise and smart eating are woven tightly, inexorably throughout.

The car, the TV, the sharp dress, the pool, the boat, the cruise, the jewels, the real estate, the amenities, accessories and extras come later, way later.

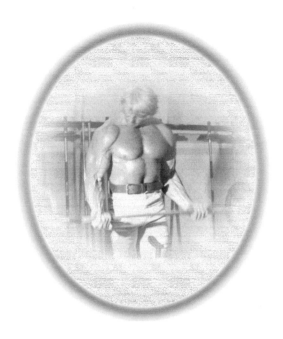

Barbells and Muscles and Those in Pursuit

As you can lead a horse to water, but you can't make him drink, so can you lead a man to weights, but you can't make him lift. He's got to be thirsty, aware and wise. You can lead the same man to the couch, TV and bowl of munchies and he'll sit, watch and eat till his belly swells and sleep overtakes him. At this practice he's a natural. As if equipped with radar, he'll locate the popular pastimes and join right in. Man is an impressive creature, capable of multitasking and very resourceful— simple, lazy, gluttonous and resourceful.

Give us, bombers all, a barbell, and throw in some dumbbells while you're at it. We'll swap the couch for an incline bench, the TV for a squat rack and the munchies for a can of tuna. You can add a bottle of spring water to the combination and we'll see you later, alligator. We've got muscles to build, power

43

to develop and a mind to challenge. We're growing by the minute! We're good.

We're also easy to please and, secretly, we're very bright. Some might call us muscleheads with a chuckle of condescension, but the joke's on them, a predicament all too obvious when they struggle to undo themselves from the couch, drag their eyes from the tube and remove their mitts from the bowl of Twinkie Dinkies. Slothfulness is addictive and achieves no good thing.

The gym, a haven featuring barbells and dumbbells, is a place of opportunity. It is what you make it, a place, in fact, for making and breaking. Know the difference! Some of us are known to attend its four walls for the single purpose of bombing and blasting the body, our ultimate intension to rip the structure of flesh and bone into shape at all cost. That sounds like fun. Pump it, burn it, load it, stretch and strain it, push and pull it, feed and starve it. Swell! Let's do that again.

Excuse me, kind sir. Such behavior sounds cruel and inhuman. What's that all about? That's simple, dear friend. More than a few lifters are a complicated mass of twisted brainwaves, dislocated emotions, faulty intelligence, fractured personalities and contradictory social indoctrinations. They're nice, but nuts.

Bodybuilders fall into this category with a thud, especially those whose eyes are on winning a big title big time. They struggle feverishly and in vain against immovable objects seeking muscle size, density, shape, symmetry, definition, skin tone, agility and power. I want it all, now. They achieve muscle tears, swollen joints and exhaustion, disillusionment, depression and despair.

There are reasons for this debacle, this complex mess, and they number in the hundreds, but be sure these trainees are in too much of a hurry for fame and glory and elusive satisfaction. They hustle the routines and schemes and diets and plans.

They force, they shove, they seek shortcuts, they eliminate common sense, they worry and they whine. The body is disregarded, the training is a suffering means and the imagined end is worshipped like a god, a golden bull. Brains go out the window and the ego bandito takes over.

I was a bodybuilder for about ten minutes, till I recognized the self-destructive nature of the beast. I now consider myself a musclebuilder, healthy, sane and free of aberration. I'm a bomber of the common denominator. Crazy but happy, paint me Stealth black.

I have a handful of friends who go to the gym to aggressively play around. They're not obsessed, driven by lofty goals and stretching for things out of reach. They simply love the energized atmosphere, the lively communication, the vigorous physical struggle and the undemanding, unstructured achievement of health, muscle and might. Lucky guys and gals, they are characters to emulate. They don't tempt disappointment, struggle and overtrain or regularly risk injury. They just… are.

They are healthy in mind, body and soul, these happy free jostlers of the iron. They don't become champions; they don't need to, they don't wish to and are not crushed when they don't. In that, they are the champions wannabe-champions will never be. Very cool.

Streaming through the doors of today's brightly lit gyms — expansive athletic clubs, trendy spas and dazzling health emporiums — are a breed of the worldwide community who pursue image and approval and identification. Looking good while pretending to exercise is good enough. They come and they go, reflections in the polished mirrors.

Not us, bombers. We come, we stay and we stay some more. We won't go; you can't make us go and, if you try to make us go, you answer to all of us, see? Now, beat it, chump, or you're in for a thump. We're losing our pump.

The tough endure, but not always the first time around the bench press. It was once said to the muscleheads of the world "If at first you don't succeed, try, try again." Scholars of the heavy art form have united and agreed this statement is a truth. Only those who persist can enjoy the grand rewards weight lifting has to offer. But it often happens that we start and stop, start and stop and start again before clutching the impervious deed and forming it to our lives. This is called supreme perseverance; that is, perseverance, stimulated by hope, accented by growing confidence, enforced with courage and practiced with heart. The muscular and well-defined quality identifies one, just one, sterling aspect of a real bomber. But you knew that.

What's that you say? If you can't do the time, don't do the crime. If you can't do the pain, don't expect to gain. If you won't strain, don't complain 'cuz you remain the same. There's a breed of lifters slipping through the gym daily who execute exercises with precision, but do not apply effort. Ha. That's like telling a joke without a punchline — no amusement, no laughter, no one rolling on the floor in uncontrollable stitches… not even a snicker. No muscles, no might.

Let's push it, girls and boys. This ain't a church social or the "Class of '96" reunion picnic; it's a stinking gym for crying out loud. This is a workout and those are dumbbells, not chrysanthemums, and them there are barbells, not hotdogs on sticks. Strain, pain, sweat and gain. It's wonderful. It's delightful. It's delirious. Try it, you'll like it. Go, you'll grow.

I'm being mean (sometimes I just can't help myself). I respect the non-aggressive trainee who displays care, consistency, discipline and good form. I merely encourage an increase in exercise output to increase the benefits of the time and attention invested. Does the wise man lower a bucket in the well only to raise the receptacle absent of cool, refreshing water?

Add effort to your performance and add power to your life. You're here: Put fire in the furnace, zeal in the steel and vim in the gym.

What is a gym, really, Mr. Fairworthy? The gym is home to the alone, a training camp to the robust, a correctional facility to the madman, a repair shop for the broken and a fairground to the lighthearted. It's a hangout, a refuge, a rendezvous and a place to regroup.

It's also an alien territory to the anxious, fearful and shy. Oh, no, not the gym! There are people there — muscular people, beautiful people, capable and confident people who know who they are, where they're going and what to say. They smile, laugh, joke and have friends. I'd rather hide under a rack than go to a gym. I wanna go home to my refrigerator.

Not exactly. People in the gym are just people with arms and legs and hang-ups, like you and me. Yeah, there are a few jerks in every gym. So what? That's life. That's their problem.

Come to think of it, there are a lot of jerks in gyms, more in some than in others. Worry not, their attention is on themselves. I'm with you, my reluctant friend, and I, too, walk circles around those people, those places. Arrogance, childishness, rudeness and ignorance are the behavior of fools. Let their poor performance strengthen your character, as the weights strengthen your muscles and bones. Neither hate them nor pity them, but surely ignore them. Maybe one day they'll grow up.

Try this. Go directly to a stationary bike, mount the darn thing and start pedaling. You did it when you were in the first grade, you can do it again. After five minutes of exercise you'll no longer care who's on the floor, how swell they are, how much they weigh or where they're looking. You're exercising. You're distracted, involved, working, progressing and invigorated. You're high. Exercise does that, among other things.

No way, you say? Alrighty, then; you might consider a personal trainer to get you through the initial steps, hurdles, hoops, tricks and treats of your first gym experience. Three comprehensive training sessions from a trainer who has lifted his or her share of the iron off the Earth's surface (not just read about it) should provide the boldness and knowledge you need to move the heavy stuff till you can lift it on your own. Check in with your mentor once a month for refreshment, assessment, affirmation and further consultation to keep you strong and on track. Now you're going places and as fast as you can go. Drink your protein shake and keep smiling.

Yes, the world is made up of all types. You and me, for example, sterling characters, devoted and wise, caring and generous. Let us continue to frequent the gym that we may inspire others, teach them, set them in motion and direct their ways. It's our duty, our calling, our promise.

Yeah, right. If I don't go to the gym, I go to jail, rehab, the streets and alleys, the county institution for the muttering; I twitch and I drool. My duty is to blast it, my promise is to get huge and my calling is Bombs Away.

Today is the day before tomorrow. Don't miss it, bombers, like it was the day before today. Start your engines. Take her up, take her high and look around you; listen to the roar, feel the wind on your face, hold her fast 'n' steady and land her safely. We want to do this again tomorrow and for the rest of our lives. It's our gift.

The First Cut is the Deepest

When we are directed to press on and never look back, the concept imparted is to strive forward with hope, courage and intelligence and not dwell on the blunders of the past. We tend to condemn ourselves for our faults and failures till they are etched in our minds and form the indelible impression of a broken, unfixable self. The longer we support this habit of wrong thinking, the less able and willing we are to restore ourselves and get a life.

Guilt and fear stemming from neglect, failed workout attempts and the subsequent unconditioned state of our being prevent us from confronting our limp and lumpy condition. Weak, whiny thoughts such as "Muscles and might are for the athletic types, not me" and "I'll get to it later," or "Why bother?"

undermine effective steps toward our fitness and health. Negative thinking is for fools. Not us.

Be bold. Start immediately with resolve. Be enthusiastic. Start with the hopeful spirit of a wide-eyed child. When no one else is looking, remove all junk foods from the cupboards, counter tops and refrigerator.

Once you've cleared the table, and the stores of non-nutritious and sugary food and drink have been restricted and properly replaced with high protein foods for musclebuilding, energy sustenance and appetite satisfaction, we may begin. I bow with admiration and respect for removing those destructive stumbling blocks from your path. Don't you feel great having embraced willpower and its might? The junk you discarded was a threat to your health and fitness, and its elimination represents a weak barrier torn down and a solid foundation built. The physical benefits you are about to realize are immediately before you, short- and long-term. You will notice your energy and moods stabilize and improve. This, I suspect, is due in part to the liberation from the chattering sugar-monkey on your back. Moreover, it's a welcome chemical response as your body restores its healthy metabolism, enzyme and hormone activity. Life gets better every day as commitment, determination and time lock hands. Watch the unwanted pounds drift away.

The next most important moves we need to make are physical. Are you walking and running according to the exercise revival plan you set in motion? Excellent. We must now consider what freehand exercises we can do in the comfortable and adequate confines of the home. Any and all muscle resistance works if we apply ourselves attentively, rigorously and regularly. Let's choose a handful of mild exercises that you can practice and perfect over the next few weeks. Remember, they work. You don't need a gym with elaborate equipment to get the job done.

Keep in mind you are about to take a worthy step in achieving your goal to build muscle, diminish bodyfat and set some commendable disciplines in place. Look around and select a place (bedroom, basement, garage, deck or carport) where you can privately stretch out and perform your small yet effective collection of exercises. You'll need a clear wall, two sturdy chairs, a broomstick and a small mat or rug for the floor. Today and through the weeks ahead we practice, learn and condition ourselves (joints, tendons, muscles, respiratory system and mind) as the exercises unfold. Let's go.

The wall push-away is begun by leaning ten degrees with your hands supported against your favorite wall. Bend at the elbows till the forehead touches and push away to complete one repetition. Continue for 12 to 15 reps, rest thirty seconds and repeat. The further you stand from the wall the greater the resistance on the muscles involved (triceps, chest and shoulders). Vary the width of your hand position to suit your structure and comfort, shoulder height and some six inches beyond shoulder width being standard.

Push-ups are very similar except you are lying facedown on the floor and the resistance is increased, requiring more torso and triceps effort. Arms bent appropriately at your sides and palms down, push your torso up while your knees remain on the floor. Up and down for each repetition until you count 10 reps or tire. Again, two sets (groups of repetitions) do it, sixty to ninety seconds rest between sets is suggested. As your strength increases, shift the lower body's support from the knees to the feet for added resistance. Now you're workin'.

Crossbar chin-ups require two upright chairs with a tough broomstick placed across their backs. Lying on the floor or a low support beneath the improvised apparatus, reach up and grasp the bar at shoulder width (near the chair backs) and, while the body remains rigid, pull up until the chin meets the bar. A difficult and unsure movement, the crossbar chin requires practice and persuasion before two sets of 10 to 12 reps is achieved. Work at the challenge regularly and your biceps, upper and lower back will build in health, shape and might.

The freehand squat or deep-knee bend is a very simple yet effective exercise for moving volumes of blood through the system to improve circulation and respiration. The squat has a comprehensive effect on the body and enhances its total structure and potential. Squats build strong, shapely and lasting legs from the calf to the buttocks. Stand erect with your hand on a chair back for balance. Looking straight ahead and maintaining the upright position, move your backside out, bend at the knees and slowly lower yourself until your thighs are horizontal to the floor. Without bouncing and with a slight pause, return slowly to your starting position. That's one squat. Two sets of 12 are terrific. One fine day we'll talk about the attributes of lunges and walking lunges. I know; you can't wait. There's no end to the joys of exercise, a strong body and good health.

Final notes: Focus on the task and the muscles involved. Take a deep breath before executing each repetition and exhale as you exert resistance on the return. Practice your beginning routine three days a week alternating with your running and torso exercises. Progress to three sets per exercise when you feel ready. You are training.

Spare the Rod, Spoil the Ironhead

I was out in the field patching up the old bomber the other day when it occurred to me some of you are only 20-something and to you age, the number of years you've gathered while here on earth, is rather incidental. Your birthday rolls around (once a year, as you recall) and you might fuss over a special dinner and a few cute cards, some gifts if you have those family traditions, and it goes away. If asked, you recall a spasm of transfomation when you turned 18 (I'm legal) and a feeling of melancholy at 20 when you bravely left the teens behind. But as you slip and slide in those busy, invincible and seemingly unending 20s, collecting years is no more on your mind than collecting string.

Yeah, well, live it up. 30 will probably get your attention (who am I, where am I goin' and why ain't I there yet?). And the Big Four-O is always good for a few shaky laughs and some restless days — nights, weeks, months and years (where did my life go?).

Not everyone embraces the 40s with open arms (they hide under the bed) and those truly wonderful years can cause a good man or woman to do some really strange things. They often dress funny, wear gold chains over tanned chests and accentuate the makeup; they color their hair, transplant it like the potted plants on the front porch, throw an accenting toupee over it like a politician or shave it off like the Sultan of Babawamba. The lonely adopt a golden retriever or a four-pound terrier or chase the opposite sex; there's the two-seater sports car, the nip 'n' tuck, the consuming introspection and, not infrequently, the bottle nestled beneath the undies in the laundry basket. Gulp.

Of all our pathetic blunders, the most disgraceful and distressing is losing those priceless years trying to save them. There's a problem, but we don't know what it is. We misunderstand it, attempt to hide it from view or chase it away. We need not resist the passing of time, as if life was slipping away and we were diminishing. That is to support the misperception of aging, to feed it, to fear it and become its victim. Big mistake, like allowing a spoiled child to rule us by moping and pouting or kicking and screaming to get its way.

Discipline the brat.

We see ourselves as having reached our peak after too many years of worry, sacrifice, poor choices and bad food. We further burden ourselves with fear, doubt and anxiety, the end-times gloom. It's the wrinkles, sagging skin, flaccid biceps, abounding midsection, achy back, wobbly legs and piling chins. It's over. Youth gone by, if only I knew then what I know now. It's true what they say: Youth is wasted on the young.

Phooey.

Instead, we need to recognize — awaken — the willing and able companion we are, the friend who deserves our love and encouragement and support. You're not old, I'm not old; George Washington is old. We're just kids in a body that needs our help. Get back to the gym with purpose and zeal, eat right, for cryin' out loud, and the youth that faded away will return with open arms. To outsiders I say, start exercising, today, stimulate the body, excite the soul, discover self-control and delight in the fulfillment. Get rid of the sugar, toss the junk and eat precious protein by the bunch — starting like now, today — and give your favorite body something to feed on and live for. Stop stumbling as you chase your nightmarish midlife daydreams. Grasp authentic strength, health and action with willing hands. Stand up. Be strong.

Shift gears.

Things don't go from bad to worse. They go from better than you think to terrific. The years of your life add up, yes, but you add years to your life. Youth isn't wasted on the young, nor are the 40s and 50s wasted on you. You're in control at the prime of your life with all you need to know. Fix what's broke and soup up what's workin' good. Zoom, zoom. We got places to go and things to do.

I have a special affection for those middle years, 40 to 50, because I beat the 30s, the season of the prince and princess, repeatedly with a blunt object and was reborn in the ten years that followed. I was 42, to be exact, when I got to my feet after a fall, dusted myself off, surveyed the burned-out territory in which I stood and commenced the act of walking forward, one step at a time. (The point, please, oh sorrowful fallen victim.) The 40s are really good for that sort of thing, making magnificent strides over peaks, plateaus and beast-ridden countryside and dragging what appear to be burned out carcasses back to life. The 50s work very well also, but you've got to be, like Jack, nimble and quick, alert and ready. While I'm at it, the 60s, it seems, takes a nickel from one pocket and put a dime in the other. You don't know whether to say, hey, hands off or thank you, thank you, thank you, brother time.

During the early years when we were growing up, we ate what we ate 'cuz it was there and did what we did 'cuz we were told. Later, as we got older, we imitated our surroundings, what we viewed on TV and saw in the media. For most of us, it was neither very good nor very bad. It was sufficient. Today, with the passing of time, the good has diminished and the bad has increased. We eat like horses and act like hogs; we do what is easy, what is our habit or what little we can. And we know it, we're not doing anything about it, it's not getting any better and it doesn't have to be that way.

We can control it.

I've been weight training for a long time and more or less in pursuit of muscles and strength since I was a kid. Even when I was bad and messin' up along the way, I was training and eating tuna. Talk about a dizzy dude. The last 20 years have been as straight as an arrow and I've been attentive to life around me, the days gone by and the days ahead. How to keep the stone rolling and free of moss has become my hobby. Keeping my davedraper.com website visitors periodically informed of my observations helps me observe. Evidently there's this cool group of people who care and wonder as I do. I am, therefore, accountable.

So what's the latest? Remember, dear reader whose eyes are yet to require magnifying glasses to read these pages, this stuff's for all ages and conditions, breeds, makes and models. Listen and learn, or not.

I only have positive news to report. Last spring, I added to my workout certain unpopular exercises that I had ignored for

40 years to replace those exercises that were overused, abused and not withstanding the years. The additions included low-incline flys for pecs, reverse-cable crossovers for the back and rear delts, widegrip pulldowns behind the neck and medium-wide parallel-grip pulldowns.

They have proven to be effective and productive and my strength in each movement has increased considerably. This is great news when inflammation and nerve pain due to repeat trauma — exercise redundancy — start to limit one's plane of resistance, repertoire of exercise and joy of performance. Little things started to happen and continue to happen here and there: fullness, tightness, hardness, expanded capability, comfort and reduction of "bad" pain in critical areas. The direction remains forward and upward, in spite of the wrinkles and aches time insists I bear to keep me humble and forever grateful.

Compared to my golden days, I'm a wreck. Even so, I'm stronger in squatting, pulling and deadlifting than ever before and more capable in pushing and pressing than in the last few years. The revolting nerve pain in the right wrist and elbow prevent me from demonstrating the true ability of my shoulders and triceps. Nevertheless, maximum muscle exertion in difficult regions is approachable through warm-up, focused reps, periodic forced, slow reps, modified grooves and accommodating body positioning. Pressing on is successful, development is possible. That's the point of my story, hopeful bombers, not me and my clay-footed pursuits.

We train for muscle and power, health, fun, expression, stress repression and because, once bitten, we must. When I train for maximum response, that is, muscle growth, definition, density, strength and intensity in performance, I train with ultimate focus and concentration. My attention does not veer from the work before me. To the extent that it does, the work is compromised. The physical, the mental and the emotional become entwined and tightly strung. I love my training most when it's at that level. Only then is it really training. Other times it's play.

I'll continue my juggling act and throw in a somersault every now and then — anything to keep you motivated and training and eating right.

Bombers, you're part of a grand and rare team.

The Exceptions Rule

Having come from the corners of bedrooms, garages and basements, I doubt if I know how to behave in a large gym, one of those sprawling 25-50,000-square-foot supermarket affairs, an immense room with acres of rug and black mats underfoot and florescent lighting overhead. The seasons come and go and still you can't find the Roman chair or a water fountain, a friend or a familiar face. The iron you lift shrinks in size, yet moves with increasing difficulty as its weight is compounded by its echo from across the vast gym floor. You're a flea on a big dog's back.

The gym I train in is an 8,000-square-foot shoebox with two open staircases leading to a balcony where the aerobic equipment and stretch areas are located. The railed loft is quiet and offers a broad view of the working bodies below. Once a high-ceiling warehouse, the scattered skylights and glassed-in over-sized garage doors at either end give the musclebuilding, health-seeking occupants a welcome connection to the vital outdoors — multiple freedoms united.

The other day I sat atop the staircase overlooking the length of the gym floor and gazed at the activity. I don't perform the leisure thing often 'cuz there's always something that needs to be done: blast the chest and bomb the back. However, among the things I do best, daydreaming — imaginative thinking, that is — ranks high in the top ten.

What I saw was a hopeful and warming sight, 20 or so men and women of various shapes and sizes and ages, the relative few who are faithfully following through with their health, fitness and musclebuilding programs. Now this group was not tiptoeing through the daisies or sipping on Perrier as they chatted senselessly about hemlines or stock prices.

They were working.

The energy, devotion and spirits were high and I wondered why so few, really, choose to care for themselves. I mean fewer than five out of a hundred exercise for their health and fitness, while fifty out of the same hundred smoke, drink and eat junk by the truckload.

Oddly, we as a society tend to abuse ourselves — subtly and unconsciously, or blatantly and deliberately — rather than care for ourselves; and then we hide it with clothes, make-up, attitude, drastic fix-it schemes and medications and goofy distractions. I shouldn't wonder and I don't judge (too harshly) as I have been known to wander empty wastelands for days on end myself.

Out of social convention bad habits are born. Come to think of it, social convention is a bad habit.

Let us, you and me, continue to break the common molds cast by a society that, given a choice, sits on soft pillows with one hand in a sack of (sugar-coated, deep-fried, chemical-dense, nutrient-sparse) tasty treats and both eyes glued to the screen, wasting precious time. We are all heroes and winners and champions, yet pervasive forces threaten to hold us back and bring us down, a fatigue of spirit and the gravitational pull of emotions, lethargy due to ailing creativity and apathy fed by second-hand inspiration. Too much sugar, not enough meat.

Here's our edge: Awareness of the symptoms keeps us from the sickness.

Knowing the dangers and pitfalls, we bypass the destruction. We peer at our weakness and failing, procrastination and ignorance, excuses and carelessness, lack of will and lack of incentive as if on display under sterile glass, a reminder of our past and a research project in process. We are safe, self-inoculated, humbled and mildly proud.

Here's our duty: One day at a time, with an eye on the next and a glance at the last, we put both hands to the task.

Now lift that steel and push that iron. We've got work to do, brothers and sisters. Set the direction, clear the path and be the light. We've got to shine for those who don't.

Second helpings, apple pie and chocolate sound good today, but how will they feel and look tomorrow? The price is seldom worth the experience. The guilt we carry around, not to mention the added pounds, is heavy and causes fatigue, stress and self-loathing. Who can stand up under this load?

There's no negotiating the placement of the guilt. It's where it belongs. So now what? Limit your indulgences to fewer and smaller, and accept them as part of your bigger and larger plan.

The Decline

Here is a rough bullet-summary of a devastating decline of modern mankind. Laugh it up. Pretend it's a badly scripted, poorly directed B-flick from Hollywood starring the Osmond family.

• Fitness takes hold in the '60s and erupts in the '70s. Swell. Big biz and big bucks do their dirty work: feeding frenzy, deception and hype, confusion and gluttony. No comprehensive education offered, intended or achieved, just sell, exploit, sell. Aerobics will set you free, buy a $7,000 treadmill.

• Fast food arrives in '60s — just what we needed — waistlines and appetites grow, time shrinks.

• Schools drop athletic programs and classes on nutrition. Junk food and fast food is installed in school halls and cafeterias instead.

• Fast-track living increases across the fruited plains to accommodate rising costs; God's replaced by a second job, second car, second mortgage and declining morality.

• Generation gap in understanding critical need for sound exercise and right eating widens... going, going, gone.

• Less family life, more single-parent families, less homefront education from the now nutrition- and exercise-ignorant moms and dads results in the development of horrible eating habits and passive lifestyles.

• Computers and video games replace physical play and sports for adults and kids alike. Standard game rules: 1) Sit on butt and 2) Press the buttons.

• Governments miss the picture by light-years. The FDA and other agencies are 70 years behind the times in the nutrition information they offer to the populace.

• Sugar and grain lobbyists and fast food bosses control the government and they control society, the herds, the sheep.

• Terrorism, wars, serial killers and small and large thieves — wickedness — removes the prevailing wind from the ship's sails and strain at man's hopes.

The match is not over yet. It's time to get back up and fight like a man, like a woman, right here, right now. Exercise, eat right and grin with joy, and build enabling discipline and enliven the weary character as you do.

It's easy to shine in the world today. You need a good protein-high breakfast when you rise, and four more equally nutritious meals throughout the day. Put aside that time of rejoicing alone or with like minds three or four days a week, 60 exhilarating minutes of vigorous exercise.

Do you have any idea how the simple paragraph you just read can change your life? I bet you do and you're rare. Re-read it, fifty words. Further, if you actually practice the outlined precepts, you are extraordinary and have more life here and now and before you than the poor individual to your left and right and behind you who doesn't.

This big old world was built for bombers.

Do you think nothing is happening because you don't see your expectations materialize, your hopes and fantasies come true on time? How about the vastly improved health of your heart and lungs, the balance corrections in your hormonal system, the continued development of your neurological network, the ongoing detoxifying of your body, the fat mobilizing and improved metabolization?

You overlooked the steady increase in overall strength, the increased bone density, the consistent anabolic environment working ceaselessly to repair and build muscle tissue, and the glorious feeling when another fantastic workout is done. You do remember these things, don't you?

Vanity doth hide beneath the thinnest of epidermal coverings. Oh, that I might one day be free of its calloused groping hand.

The Indoctrination of a Bomber

Compliments are hard to receive and they are often misunderstood. For example, when folks look us in the eyes and tell us we're stubborn, stiff, dull and single-minded airheads, we're caught slightly off guard — we blink, fidget and stammer. What they're really saying is we're persevering, disciplined, patient, goal-seeking positive thinkers. Thank them profusely, adding how much you appreciate their keen insight and tender encouragement. Friendships are gifts from above.

There is nothing new under the sun, bombers; you've heard it all before. But there are some things we ought to repeat regularly despite the tedium of the process. They are like reflecting lights that illuminate our way, and our way is one step from the shadow of darkness.

I'm no more serious than a clown in a bull ring. If you find this stuff rigid, it's 'cuz you're more concerned about the snorting and stomping bull than the smiley clown in the barrel. Take the next five or ten minutes to read these pages of my tiresome indoctrination; call it endurance.

Seek contentment, abhor complacency and do not be anxious about anything. The most we can expect of life is a grand virtue; living it with its hardships and joys, accumulating our time without regret and doing our best and accepting the rest; be honest, true to one's self and give no ear to our critics, who are less pleased with us than we are with ourselves. Try too hard and we fall on our backsides. Put a squeeze on time and it slips through our hands. Expect too much and our best is never enough. Steady as she goes, bombers, and she'll go a long way, high and far.

Call it perseverance, or stubborn.

Set your goals, ample and wise, and seek them with diligence and might. Be unique, be yourself, imitate no one and be kind to those who follow your ways. Work hard, eat right and be consistent, a simple practice that keeps us untethered — alive and free. Slip not into apathy, ward off lethargy and boldly resist gluttony, the shallow characteristics typical of the masses crowding our path. Don't compromise those standards set high by your spirit, mind and deeds. Clay feet we have, and soiling our neighbor is too easy to do and so hard to recall. Be careful. Be aware. Be grateful. Be emboldened and filled with joy.

Sounds like discipline and self-control to me, or maybe stiff.

Wait until you can wait no more, and wait again. Do what's right once, twice and three times. If what you do continues to be right, do it ten times more. The least you've done is something right many times, and practiced a quality of greatness that eludes most day after day. It goes by many names, a favorite of which is persistence. Be persistent always, when doing good is troublesome to do, when getting to a worthy place is doubtful and precarious and when giving up a wicked way is painful and slippery.

Courage accompanies this, an admirable weapon in our arsenal. You've heard of fortitude and marveled at its name. Oh, to have fortitude each morning when the sun rises and each evening when the sun goes down. Nothing wretched before us could endure.

Could be patient, could be dull.

Living without constraints and wandering freely are priceless lifestyles with immediate rewards. Looking and seeing, listening and hearing, we learn, imagine, discover, wonder, invent, play and pretend. It's fun. Yet, without aspirations toward which to direct our steps, we go nowhere, get nothing done and accomplish little. To grow we need a place to go, a purpose to achieve, a target to seek.

Aimlessness and wandering take us around and about, backwards and sideways, but they don't move us forward. They don't get us ahead. They don't fulfill our longings. First objective, bombers: keep our eyes on the fuel gauge, air speed and altimeter. Ultimate objective: reach our destinations.

This one is definitely, without a doubt, goal-seeking and single-mindedness.

Once we know where we are going and how to get there — decisions made with no small amount of planning and wisdom — we might consider engraving them on our foreheads or tattooing them on our chests. They are that important. Better yet, imagining our goals and the might employed in gaining them will be far more efficacious to bring them to bear than bizarre physical reminders. We must see what we want clearly, vividly, passionately in our imaginations, and our creative subconscious minds will set to the task of accomplishing the job placed before them.

Our brains, conveniently and carefully located in our relatively small heads, are sophisticated, goal-seeking computers ready to do wonders based on the information we feed them. Feed them well — no garbage, like doubt or fear or despair — and they will amaze us with their integrated, highly technical capacity to achieve our goals. We're smarter than we think.

We want something, know what we want and want it badly. Good. This will help us achieve it. Incidentally, we must be certain what we want "badly" is "good." We don't want something we ought not to want, like the money in the local 7/11 cash register or Bobby's girl or several pizzas and beer. We have a way of rationalizing our wants and confusing them with our needs or possibilities. At 40 or 50, guys, don't expect a huge and ripped body capable of squatting 505 and running the 100-yard dash in 10-flat. Unlikely. And, girls, 36-26-36 at 46 is another unlikely.

Disclaimer: The above accomplishments are achievable by daring athletes.

As in everything we do, be real. Let's, for example, strive for a strong, well-built body, which is about as good as "good" gets. Now, practice the visualizing process described above. See, feel, taste, smell and wear that mighty sight as if it were your own. I don't mean get all goofy like a little kid, but close is not a bad idea. Determine the methods required to achieve your goals and implement them with resolve. Know that wavering in your pursuit is foolish, weak and damning to the process.

There'll be times when we give up, no longer care, get sidetracked, misplace inspiration, lose ambition, get lazy, procrastinate, encounter the blues or fall into a slump. That's life, either an affliction or a challenge. Afflictions attack the weak and take them down; challenges are moments of truth subject to the strong. Push on, press on; tug, pull and squeeze with all your might. The day is ours, by God, to add to our riches. Don't waste it; make the best of it, smooth its course with repeated treading. Dedication and devotion, they beat like resonant drums.

Absolutely committed, or idiotic. Yup!

At birth we're given a miracle to enjoy, cherish and care for. We call it life. Nothing compares to its splendor and supremacy.

We are guided in our understanding of and regard for life by those before us, our inherent instincts and our ensuing common sense. Somehow we miss the living picture, seeing only an occasional snapshot and a hazy one at that. Eventually our care for our lives — our body, our mind, our behavior, our direction — and the lives of those around us falls short of its basic requirements and we allow it to slip away. Physical health deteriorates as we daily misfeed and mistreat it; the mind suffers as it is neglected or stressed and overworked; our emotions are abused by wrong thinking, and we run off in different directions looking for wealth and unrequited fulfillment and pleasure.

"Neat gift," some say, "think I'll destroy it. In my toolbox I have donuts and soda pop, drugs and alcohol and cigarettes, jealousy and envy and greed. That should get me started. How about you? There's a guy with scams and lies and petty gossip. Swell!"

And the ball keeps rolling along... bumpity bump.

Man eats like a hog; he's lazy and apathetic; he's rude and self-serving; he disregards and procrastinates and he looks for the easy way out. Many of our wrong-doings, should we take notice, are unintentional mistakes due to ignorance. They are accidents, not premeditated crimes. This is no excuse, reason or rationale. And it doesn't mean a crime has not been perpetrated, and on an inexcusable daily basis.

It's a sad and simple fact of life, that same life we should honor and protect: Respect has become lost in the jungle.

This one is irresponsible, boneheaded and very uncool.

When will we get our act together, people? Gratefully, we are bombers who are miles ahead and above the masses of whom I speak, and our ways are virtuous in comparison. We try hard to do it right, we falter and try again. We're getting there by confidence, knowledge and encouragement... and by the corny hot-points outlined above.

Bombers, prepare for takeoff. We've got places to go, things to do and sights to see.

Training Motivators

It's my love for the activity of weight lifting and the great feelings and rewards surrounding health and strength and exercise execution that have kept me close for so long. Herein lie the primary motivations.

I like it, it feels good and it's good for me.

The most effective secondary motivator for us, having trained and known the good feelings of conditioning oneself and being in condition, is to contemplate what happens if we don't continue in our attitude and practice of training and eating right. Look around and without being cruel, how do you describe your neighbor on the street? Apart from the rare exception and unless he or she is a young person (and this, no longer an acceptable criteria), he or she is probably under-muscled and underpowered, unhealthy, limited and negligent. Is that someone with whom we want to identify?

He's ignorant and unaware and undisciplined and lazy and a conformist. Sounds cruel, I agree, but his condition is a reflection of his values and purpose. He's not unlike everyone else. He's got a job and aspirations and friends, perhaps, but he's ignoring his greater treasures and gifts — his health, long life, vitality, physical might and ability, personal power and enthusiasm and creative thinking. He's there, limited by himself, doing, yet winding down. He's neglecting his body, an intricate and miraculous system of flesh, bones and muscles, electricity, brain waves, glands, hormones and pulsing life. That's a shame, a loss, a crime and a sin.

You who stumble over your exercise and menu, where will you be next week, at Christmas or a year from now? Will you be blending in with the unknowing and uncaring puppets around you, bumping into furniture and bouncing off walls? Day by day neglect pervades; it gets worse, less tolerable, harder to confront and more difficult to fix. It eats you alive physically and emotionally and is evident in your personality, thinking, appearance, performance and spirit. Darkness, darkness, is there no light?

There's motivation in that black tale of defeat. Put those healthy, friendly, comforting practices you're familiar with back into play and the multiplicity of deterioration stops short, reverses immediately and your very own goodness returns, as sure as the sun rises in the morning. The process is not magical nor does it occur overnight, but it is certain and that's good enough for me and you and the man in the moon.

You stumbling? Do this: Put aside an hour a day for as many days a week as you can, a minimum of three. This is your precious time to train. Acknowledge it, respect it, be thankful for it, use it. It should not be a severe, austere hour and not a casual hour, but one of dedication and exhilaration. Forget aerobic exercise for now and get into the business of basic musclebuilding. Let your continued training and smart eating diminish the fat while you build strong muscle by pushing the iron.

Keep it pure and simple, the basic exercises work best — more punch with less set-up time and frivolity. Do what you know and like most, seek balance and don't try to do it all. It's important and most effective to be focused, content and un-hurried, yet following a good pace with good form. Haste makes waste. Hurry makes one anxious, stressed, and is counterpro-ductive. Relax and train hard and enjoy it. Remember, you want to get a grasp on your training and want to enjoy it before lousing it up with lots of pressure and demands (bigger guns, more cuts, etched abdominals, big bench, competition), which leads to disappointment and overload and injury and quitting. You can alter your training scheme down the line — be grate-ful for steady and pleasurable training. You're back in the saddle again, cowboys and cowgirls.

When we enjoy our work, missions and projects, we don't need motivators. We do them because we like them. School, study, the job, yardwork — to some folks these are a joy, re-warding and fascinating and satisfying. Discover in your exer-cise plan — your training — these characteristics and attrac-tions. They are there. Fashion or re-fashion your powerful and worthy fitness endeavor to be interesting, meaningful, stimu-lating, exhilarating and challenging. This requires common sense — next to a dog, man's best friend — and a little analysis and effort.

Keep your eye on the purpose and rewards during those moments you feel the steel and execute an exercise. Contract and extend, pump and burn, seek form and establish pace. Wake up, look up, step up and build up. That you have the perception of lifting weights and smart eating and the means and the ability to practice them are gifts. Enjoy the iron, and the might to push it. Savor the proteins and tantalizing disciplines. It only gets better and better every day... unless, of course, you interfere with wrong thinking, old habits and lost courage.

Like it or not we each have an image of our self and we respond to it. That image can be accurate or inaccurate; we tend to become who we think we are. Be careful of what you think of yourself. You might become a scoundrel, a loud mouth or a portly and complacent loser. Adjustments are at your fingertips, bombers. It's a stray from the well-traveled road to run a mile down it, to grab a bar by its girth and extend it victoriously in the air overhead, to pit your body with all your might against nearly immovable objects, to apportion an hour a day to tire yourself in good battle under the weight of heavy, lifeless metal and to insanely strain with pain to gain the edge.

Isn't that motivation enough: to stray from the norm, to strain to gain, to extend, to battle and seek the edge?

Is that too much?

The food thing is interesting. Feed me, that I might forget my plight, salve my rebelling emotions, achieve a moment of pleasure amid the daily burdens and toil, satisfy an addiction, occupy my troubled mind and avoid a responsibility. Ah, yes, I understand it serves to fuel and sustain my body as well... how convenient.

Right eating is as essential as clean air and pure water. Smart eating is as simple as arithmetic, one plus one equals two. Regular meals throughout the day, lots of protein (meat, fish, poultry, eggs and dairy) and salads and less sugar and enough fats and no overeating adds to good health and long life. Yes, discipline is required, that beautiful quality we develop with the artful assistance of patience and commitment. Their development is another powerful motivation to add to the list.

Bright stars, they account for success and achievement in all areas of our lives. They are a crown worn by the noble and dauntless, the respected and admired.

There's an abundance of healthy, mouth-watering, inexpensive and easy-to-prepare foods available in the marketplace today; thus, no excuse to compromise nutritional goodness due to the denial of tasty delights. Our urgent needs for health and weight control have alerted our social benefactors and business merchants, and reached the market shelves, eateries and restaurants. Partake, enjoy and don't overindulge. It's simple and easy.

Where are we? You want, I want, we all want a body to die for; to win the hearts and minds of the opposite sex, to win the respect and fear of the same sex; to attain general health and well-being and long life; to gain the ability to lift large and heavy objects for work, play, survival and showing off. We aspire!

Some tell me lists are for stiffs and monotonous bores. I like lists. So, here's a long list of training motivators — incentives to work out and eat right by — presented for the curious mind:

• Are you guilty of self-neglect and low-esteem? Work out and eat right. The duo effectively fights enemies and conquers foes of all manners.

• Are you a confused and disorderly person? Working out is actively meditative and restores thy soul.

• Are you sluggish? Exercise and right eating generate energy, endurance, hormonal balance, healthy digestion and clear thinking. They build and rebuild, and deter destruction.

• Are you well fed, but hungry? A workout satisfies your appetite. The joy of fulfillment from a workout well executed is indescribably delicious. A workout poorly executed is more rewarding than any dessert.

• Are you uninterested in healthy food? A workout arouses a real desire to eat.

• Are you broken? A workout is the fix.

• Are you bored? Weight lifting is a fun, fulfilling diversion.

• Are you lonely? A workout is a swell companion.

• Are you tired? A workout stimulates.

• Are you wired? A workout promotes rest and relaxation.

• Are you anxious, nervous or strung out? A workout soothes and untangles the mess.

• Are you troubled and unsure? Problems are solved while working out.

• Are you fearful and worrisome? The workout dispels this paranoid misplaced pair.

• Are you doubtful? Work out and doubt is gone.

• Are your emotions erratic? Work out. Stabilize them with active, physical confrontation.

- Are you achy and suffering general malaise? The prescription is a caring workout.

- Are you sniffling with a cold? A gentle workout stimulates the immune system.

- Are you in love and broken hearted? Go to your sweetheart and tell him or her you love 'em and can't be without 'em. Your workout can wait... unless he or she wants to join you, encourage you, spot you, assist you in loading and unloading the bars, count your reps, admire your form.

Life's motivators vary with time and age and the panorama. But health and fitness, muscles and might are a loyal and consistent troop of incentives and stimulators. Coddle them now, curry their favor, set them in stone and they, like your friends and loved ones, will never leave your side.

The hangar will remain open 24 hours to accommodate the anticipated influx of revived and highly motivated bombers. Soar high and always.

How do you judge or critique your training sessions? Do you base it on sets and reps accomplished, one-rep max achievements, manifest pump or its mere completion without collapsing from fatigue, pain or boredom? For some folks success depends on with whom they walk out door or how many laughs they had, considering they didn't drop a weight on their foot.

Sometimes a good laugh fits right in, and I try to keep the equipment off my feet and walking out the door the same way I came in is very cool always. Sets and reps are recorded in the rhythmic section of my brain and that one-rep max is always delightful, a joy to behold. I save those rascals for days when I feel invincible and failure is not a one-rep possibility.

What really does it for me is focus from beginning to end, start to stop: total concentration on each set, every deliberate rep, every calculated pause. Between sets I recover intentionally, carefully assess the work done and prepare myself purposefully for the work to come — a world of involvement. What hurts, where's the burn and how's the pump? Note the groove, the contraction and extension, and smartly direct the resistance to the preferred or needy muscle region.

Pace is important, intensity within the straining fibers, never taking your eyes off the premise: building further the muscle and might and discipline of lifting.

Exhilarating. Rewarding. Absolute.

Between these things, I daydream, nod off or whatever.

Another Month

Another day. We get up in the morning, shake off the dust, splash water on our faces and get into our rags. What happens from there is random chaos. With few exceptions we have an idea what to expect, the same ole', same ole' — have breakfast, hop in the car, fight the traffic, battle the crowds, get to work, do our jobs, win a few, lose a few, eat, laugh, grumble, mumble and home again. Phew! If married, it's the spouse and, maybe, the kids, dinner, TV and bed. Shelter, family, food, clothes, job and life. That's all it takes, that's all there is. Thank heaven.

However, some of us rise in the morning, arouse the amazing structure of flesh and bone surrounding us and say, good morning, partner, what's shakin'? Remember our agreement; I take care of you and you take care of me. We have places to go and things to do and we want to do them right. And to do them right we need the right stuff: energy and endurance for starters; strength and courage are a big help, and intelligence and common sense are particularly welcome. Let's eat.

The six qualities directly mentioned above do not grow on trees. They are not free, you can't buy them; they can't be found under a lucky rock and they are not won by chance. No begging will gain them. They are awakened, formed and developed as we aspire. And I believe — perhaps you agree — the Big Six are born and carefully cultivated as they are painfully applied in the man-size manufacturing plants known as gyms, not to be confused with colorful high-tech playpens full of toys and noise, girls and boys.

This day will not be done well, nor the days to follow, unless we go to the gym and train hard, unless we eat right when it's the right time to eat. Seriously, do you want to be a mover and shaker, on the cutting edge, one of those who are on the same page and push the envelope; you want to think out of the box and make things happen? Clue: The answer is no. That's why you go to the gym: to stray from the norm, avoid the mob and be free of cliche, to assure you do not get with the program or have another double non-fat cappuccino typical of the monkeys on the cutting edge.

You know the basic rules of exercise: 1) train at least three alternate days a week for 60 to 75 minutes, 2) be consistent, 3) chose a balanced routine to include all muscle groups, 4) be engaged — train with form and focus at a moderate pace, 5) exercise with purpose and vigor, and 6) feed yourself appropriately before and after the workout for maximum benefit and well-being.

Swell, but there's more to apple pie than apples and crust. Each one of the six basics could use some elaboration and clarification, and a little more time in the oven.

1) Training occasionally is not training at all. It's like scratching an itch, or rather, scratching a sore. Nothing is satisfied, only irritated. Commit to regular exercise as you commit to career, family and friends. Only then, with time and sweet sacrifice, will it develop and become worthy and wonderful. Training, like your body, mind and soul, is meant to last a long, long time.

Monday, Wednesday and Friday has a nice swing to it. I personally like Monday, Tuesday and Thursday, Friday — quite solid. Weekend workouts, plus one or two during the week for stability, can be fun. Get in there, do it with completeness and order and get out, picking up as much good and satisfaction as you can along the way. The harvest is bountiful.

2) Without consistency we suffer guilt and frustration and achy muscles; we create large training gaps and exercise confusion, and achieve nothing more than distraction. I wrapped up in one sentence a lethal dose of life's daily poisons. We set out to improve our physical and mental health, only to gag on a weak solution.

Make time or lose it.

Regular and progressive training rewards us with strength and health in all dimensions of our being. Day by day we add to the structure, and the structure adds to itself. Be consistent and you pick yourself up. Be inconsistent and you let yourself down.

3) Choosing a routine is simple. As a beginner you turn to your manual, routine #1, and do one exercise for each muscle group as suggested, one to three sets of 8 to 10 reps. In a month that which was foreign is friendly. You proceed to routine #2, gulp, and in 30 days that which was difficult is easy.

And so it goes. With each workout and the passing of time, understanding and knowledge accumulate. You move on, stronger and more capable. Your muscles grow.

It's when the accumulation of muscle and strength do not correspond to your expectations that choosing a routine becomes confounding; you doubt your understanding and knowledge and the rising of the sun.

Now is the time for *Brother Iron Sister Steel*, my earlier book on weight training. You are arriving. You're a bomber recruit. Welcome aboard.

4) Engagement in your workout, unlike going through the motions to get it over with, requires attention and desire. Engagement — involvement — is certain wherever enthusiasm abounds. Enthusiasm is a wonderful state of being. It suggests inspiration and energy, prime factors for joyful living, aspiration and achievement. And progress is sure when this fire of the mind and spirit is applied.

When not present on its own, the fire needs to be kindled and fueled with a disciplined and positive mind. This is deliberate and dedicated work. This man-made fire is also known as attitude. Get your attitude together, bombers. Spread your wings, if you want to fly.

5) About purpose: Let's assume you know why you're training. It's a large and important theme and if it escapes you at the moment, there's not enough time, space, energy or patience to discuss it. About vigor: Exercise that is not vigorous is like ice cream without cold and sweet. Eat all you want, but it's no fun and not at all satisfying. Over the years, as a trainee, a trainer and a gym owner, I've noticed that the major ingredient missing in most folks' workouts is intensity. And training intensity largely determines the advancement one makes toward one's goals: weight loss, conditioning, increased muscle mass and strength, improved muscle shape and tone.

Tricky term, training intensity. It's subjective and what is hard to one trainee is mild to another. And where some can and should train hard, others cannot, nor should they. Workout intensity needs to match the individual, his health and ability, and his goal. However, intensity should at least be considered by the person standing before the iron. It should be sought, calculated and wisely applied.

Blasting it is not for everyone, but a little snap, crackle or pop every now and then would be welcome. Can we please see an authentic wince of pain and hear an honest though muffled groan, iron-warrior? There ya go... very cool.

Too often it appears the lifter is taking the path of least resistance back to the lockerroom. Cute, but no cigar. The idea is to choose the path of greater resistance with challenge and aggression, common sense and intention. Now you're on the direct route to your goal, which has nothing to do with the lockerroom or juice bar or exit or gabbing or flirting. No pain, no gain. No sweat, no get.

It's the muscle overload derived from intense training that causes hypertrophy, which we commonly know as bigger and stronger and shapelier muscle. Anything less should be considered muscle massage, conditioning, practice, socializing, make-believe or a C−.

There's the other end of the pulley. Too much lifting intensity can cause burnout, injury, fatigue and overtraining. Intensity: To what degree do we apply it, when and where, and at what time do we ease up? Who said weight lifting is simple? It makes rocket science look like a dominoes. Stay tuned for more training insight, bombardiers.

6) How we eat has become contentious and a worldwide topic of conversation. Most of us know what to do, but are too lazy or undisciplined or uncaring to do it. It's pitiful and we all pay. So much for ranting, nobody loves a ranter. Let's move onward to encouragement, information and advice.

We want to enjoy our workouts, to train with high spirits, well-being and a good head of steam. Training with energy and endurance, striving beyond the burn and achieving a good pump contribute to great and productive workouts. Without proper pre-training fuel, these preferred training conditions are unlikely. In fact, quite the opposite occurs: sluggishness, disappointment, irritability and muscular deterioration are common side effects. A twelve- to sixteen-ounce protein shake thirty minutes before a workout replaces disaster with the time of your life.

And you don't go across town to the gym, park the car, jump in your gear, hit the weights, whimper like a big baby, shower and fight the traffic going home for nothing. You want lean muscles fast, right? Have a post-workout protein shake within 30 minutes of your last set of forced reps for quick recovery, an amazing body and, of course, your beloved country.

Finally, about rest, bombers: relax and sleep tight.

Fly your sturdy craft high, measure the horizons and count the stars. Life is grand.

Aren't You Glad You're a Bomber?

You don't take your bow to an empty field and randomly shoot arrows in the air, do you? You do! Well, so much for my brilliant analogy. Let me put it another way. When Tiger Woods steps onto the course and Ts his ball, a specific goal consumes his mind, doesn't it? He chooses his club, addresses the ball, concentrates deeply and swings with just the right amount of force and finesse to put the ball into the distant cup. Without the goal, he might just as well have selected a baseball bat in place of a nine iron, a Bocci ball in place of a golf ball, and beat the thing into the grass rather than seeking a hole-in-one or par for the course. He could have stayed home, sold a Buick or made a commercial; it wouldn't matter without the goal.

"Tiger beats Bocci ball into fairway with baseball bat at Pebble Beach. Fans cheer."

What's the world coming to? You've gotta have goals, bombers — big ones and small ones. That's an ever-present part of my message. What are our goals?

Our goals are piled high like apple pie in the sky. Oh, my! (I studied under Dr. Seuss.) We train to get in shape and stay in shape, get healthy and stay healthy, lose fat and stay lean, get strong and stay strong. We exercise to improve our well-being and impress our peers, overcome disabilities and diminish limitations, increase vigor and gain confidence, develop discipline and sharpen character, be more decisive and less divisive. The act itself, seeking admirable goals, makes us better people. We lift for the challenge, wellness, goodness, fun, diversion and fulfillment.

Isn't it remarkable? I'm not inventing this stuff, these are not my imaginings, and I'm not even exaggerating. I'm stating some seldom-considered facts. Each item listed is true and right on, whether it's a predetermined goal or not. If they aren't on your list of training goals, add them — free of charge. They belong there.

How about specific goals? You know, to win a contest, look slick at the beach, break a state powerlifting record, climb Mount Fuji, scare your mother-in-law or rob a liquor store?

Goals become more understandable and real when they are envisioned and dwelled upon; they gain substance and structure and direction as they are managed and examined. And no longer are they simply goals when you discuss them in tangible terms with friends; they become commitments under construction awaiting the passage of time — they are the real thing happening.

Your goals, objectives and purposes, when considered with honesty and passion, are truly inspiring. And the greater the consideration and passion, the greater the motivation and the reality of accomplishment.

Got musclebuilding goals? (Please, don't say no.) Make them work for you like the burly, handsome Clydesdale draft horses that pull brewery wagons stacked with kegs of beer across the countryside. They love to work and flex their muscles, strut and toss their heads, whinny and snort proudly. I don't think it's the beer.

In seeking my specific goal, I do nothing different. I allow the goal to sit in the driver's seat and take control around the turns and up the slopes. I suspect training finesse and order and pace will increase as the target date approaches. My focus will subtly sharpen and my mood will rise with the added pitch of adrenalin. The menu will be the same, though an unconscious tightening will be applied. There will be no misplaced workouts, no temptation to risk injury, no far-fetched powerlifting, no devastation — only sound, near-sane training.

Tracking down a special objective — for a month, for a cause, I can do this. It's fun and revealing and fortifying. It's worthwhile. Goals are a must.

Of course, if your goals are far-fetched, unreasonable or silly, they will be costly and painful obstacles to your progress. They will cause you grief and disappointment: injury, lost confidence, confusion and apprehension. These are not the teammates you want hanging around your corner of the playground. You must experience them, however, to know them, and then you must eliminate them before they become troublesome thugs. Beat it, ya bums.

Above and beyond making goals, make smart goals, or realistic goals, as they're called in success books: big ones or long-term goals and small ones or short-term goals. Zoom, zoom!

A final thought: Folks without goals are aimless and lost. Though they might possess character and strengths, the absence of a solid goal allows their potentials to go untapped, undeveloped and unrealized. They wander about looking and acting foolish. They waste time with trivial distractions, accomplish nothing, develop bad habits and eventually get in trouble. Without a purpose a person sadly contracts laziness, an insidious sickness of the mind, body and will. They do the bare minimum to make it through the day and wonder why life is so unfair, dull and woeful. Apathy takes up residence in their flesh like an impoverished transient. Cynicism fills their voices.

I'm getting depressed.

Aren't you glad you're a bomber? You have smart and solid goals of assorted shapes and sizes in various stages of completion. You're constantly planning, applying, developing, advancing, enjoying, overcoming, discovering and growing. Occasionally you lose some ground, take a step back, slip up and fall down. Good for you. You had me worried there for a second. "How will they learn to get up?" I wondered; "When will they practice humility?"

A strong craft on a good journey is awesome.

Away from the Maddening Crowd

Ever find yourself sitting quietly on your favorite bench away from the activity on the gym floor and wondering what exactly are all these people doing there? Of course not, you're healthy; but I do. I'm deranged, paranoid and lonely. Two more sets before another amazing workout is complete, I feel like a million (wiped out, aching and red-eyed) and a generous calm has flooded my pulverized body. Who are they, where do they come from and what are they doing here?

More specifically I ask, "Why does a person go to a gym?"

1) For appearance: to look trim, cool, attractive and shapely

2) To be bad: huge and tough or sexy and foxy

3) To be healthy and vital: lean, energetic, happy

4) Out of fear or guilt: he's a wreck or becoming one and can't stand it anymore

5) By doctor's orders: poor health due to inactivity (overweight, diabetes, failing heart)

6) To join a friend: friendly persuasion, to accommodate or please a mate

7) To socialize: make a friend, boy-girl action, join the fun, identify

8) To rehabilitate an injury or recover from an ailment

9) To conquer diminishing health, loss of muscle and strength, energy and personal control due to age or inactivity

10) To become a better person, inside and out: enthusiastic, disciplined, vital, strong-muscled and enduring

11) By virtue of personal responsibility: caring for one's health, ability and well-being

12) To improve one's abilities in other sports and recreational activities

13) To live longer and enjoy an independent and more abundant life

14) Because there's a cheering challenge and fulfillment in the tough experience of weight lifting, exercise and action. Each workout is fun (in odd and different ways, discovered day by day) and profusely rewarding.

15) Because the Mr. Big Boy or Ms. Cool Chic is coming up next month he or she's gotta get ripped

16) 'Cuz the state powerlifting, weight-toss, Olympic lifting and Strongman contests are right around the corner and he wants to win all four

17) Because he's been lifting weights for 10, 20, 30, 40 years and can't stop his ongoing training any more than he can stop an oncoming train. He needs it bad.

18) To stay fit and healthy, dutifully, enjoyably, without undue labor or the miseries of letting go

19) In response to pressure from society: media, talk shows, human-resource proclamations, family and friends — conformity, the right thing to do

20) 'Cuz the word is out that there are invaluable benefits at one's fingertips the moment one enters the gym, from musclemaking to long life, from moral fiber to joie de vivre

Anybody you know? Everyone is different, head to toe, fingerprint to DNA, mind to soul, personality to possibility, needs to desires, and experiences to expectations.

What are their expectations, to what level do they apply themselves, how committed are they and how committed do they become? Hmm... I watch, assess and hit another set before I'm busted or lose my pump.

She's been coming for years, three or so, and has gained direction and form. When she first walked the floor, her steps were tentative and her expression was fearful. Within a month I knew this one would stick; she needed it, her face showed it, she wasn't young and exercise gave her hope. She was a bit lonely, I guessed, and I saw some youth returning to her eyes and to the curves on her body. This day, three years later, she appeared younger, stronger, brighter and more certain.

This middle-age gal came for physical and emotional restoration and to confront and overcome some hurts and losses. You're right, what do I know? She is ten times more a person than she was or was becoming last year, I can tell you that. The gym opened the door just enough to let her in and set her free. She likes being alone and moves with a sure pace and she looks good. Still don't know her name, but I like her. Let's call her Proud Mary.

One more set and I'm outta here. The last set counts, big time, like the exclamation point at the end of a declarative statement.

Now that guy comes to the gym to unwind and rewind. He works at the American Airline counter at San Jose International, checking in travelers and attending their needs. Long hours, long drive, long lines, long faces — sorry, Ma'am, your flight has been cancelled.

The weight room provides comfort, order, a noisy privacy and the mindless task of pushing and pulling, stretching and straining. He counts his sets and reps with familiarity, unthreatened by a one-rep max or tight supersets. He's 40, in good shape — no gut, sufficient muscle and strength, no need for guns or striations — loves his wife and kids and wraps up his stress in neat piles of iron and steel. He reads *Newsweek* between sets (I frown on this, but...) and will pull out his cell-phone any minute if the rest of the gym members don't huff. Other than that, he's cool. I don't know his name either. How about Captain America?

Gathering my training gear together is not exactly a simple chore. It's scattered across the gym floor like tangled cars and rooftops after a tornado, water bottle under the squat rack (I thinks that's mine, or maybe it's Andy's), belt's hanging over the bench press, elbow and wrist wraps dangling from the dipping bars and there's my thick-bar attachment leaning against the cable-crossover. Where's my chalk? Can't leave without my chalk. Another day on the battlefield.

I've known this lady since the gym opened fifteen years ago; taking the gym away from her would be cruel and un-usual punishment. She loves this stuff like a geologist loves rocks, and digs around barbells and dumbbells with similar interest and intent. A female bulldozer, moving, unearthing, piling, shift-ing and replacing. Metal goes up and down, cables and pulleys load and unload; she tugs and stacks, pushes and racks. Every bodypart is worked with precision and passion and the effect on the 50-something structure is inspiring — a strong, well-balanced and sculpted form natural as gleaming river rock. You can call her Sue, but that's not her name.

Before I hit the road I am obliged to serve the nutritional needs of my body. The tall order is composed of a two-scoop protein shake and a small pop-top of tuna. Whatta combo, just what the doctor ordered. Yummy and it's good for me, too. While I contemplate the fare, I can't help but notice the big guy who comes from work every day at this time. He cruises the stationary bike for twenty minutes, mixes his abs with his stretching for ten and hits a total of twenty sets of weighted exercises. He wants results bad — power, size, shape and mus-cularity — and is consistent in his efforts. Been nine years according to my calculations and he's done his share of research and experimentation. He's doing fine, though he could use less mind, more heart and increased intensity.

Truth is the man wrestles with a demon: He smokes like a chimney and can't stop. It's killing him; he knows it, we talked and he's "bad addicted." Too many years on the sucking end of a Camel, the household and his companions smoke and he hasn't been cut deep enough... yet.

"I neither win nor lose the fight," he says, the thought being that training and right eating sort of neutralize or diminish the negative effects of the sticks. "I'll just keep plugging along and quit when the time is right."

Yeah. I've been there with the booze, Smokey. Time flies! Extinguish the butt before the butt extinguishes you.

Traffic's never very good in my coastal neighborhood unless you travel between one and three in the morning. I've got five miles to go and it might take me 20 to 50 minutes this afternoon, depending on the surf and tides, stars and the moon risings.

That guy by the adjustable incline is new; that is, I've never seen him here before. He's spent time in a gym in the past; I can tell by the way he moves, though I'd guess it's been years. Like riding a bike, he has the approach down, but he's a little wobbly making it up the hills. Guessing again, I'd say he needs to accept his extended absence from the weights and adjust to his less-than-impressive return: very difficult, mostly disappointing and painfully instructive. If he's got the mettle, he'll stick it out. He's 30-ish, carrying a spare, probably married with a kid or two and at least one job, what Zorba the Greek referred to as "the whole catastrophe."

Nothing will be more valuable to him and his family than his successful re-entry into the world of health and fitness, exercise and eating right. I'll spare you the rhetoric. Let's just say it's more valuable than a hefty pay raise, a sparkling new sports car, a college degree in this 'n' that, a case of protein (close call) or a cozy lakeside bungalow in Northern California.

Good luck, Charlie Brown. The world is counting on you — you and all you former dropouts from Nova Scotia to San Juan, from the Straits to the Keys, Baghdad to Buenos Aires. No one can say I don't know my geography.

Isn't it a thrill, bombers, to fly above the turbulence, know where you're going and why? The fuel's not free, the stabilizers need occasional adjustment and the cockpit is a little tight at times... but we soar, by God.

Discipline is one of the most valuable qualities one can possess. Like a tree, you start with a seed; you plant it and grow it.

You develop discipline — it is not a gift, an inheritance or a purchased commodity. And was it a tree, its fruits would be perseverance and patience.

Discipline is not owned by repeating mantras, reading a book, watching a video or following a formula. Discipline is founded in need and desire and developed in deed.

Here's the seed... take it to the gym and plant it in the most fertile of soils, beneath the iron and steel.

Lack of Motivation

Staying motivated when the world is coming down on all sides is a problem many of us face regularly. We don't have to go very far before we trip over an obstacle, encounter a detour or fall into a deep, fiery pit where monsters live. Whether getting to the gym across town, entering the foreboding doors to the iron tonnage in the garage or approaching the bench in the basement — AKA, the torture rack — heaviness in the heart and mind is like lead in the seat of our underpants. I want candy, TV and the couch, you think, but your fat and skinny conscience fights like a frenzied dog.

You're a tough one; you made it and there they are, the rolly-polly weights and all the neat benches, pulleys and gadgets you could think of, ready for action. You say, why me, why today… why? Because, that's why. Why is the sky blue? Because, that's why. You don't need an answer; the answer is in the first set. You're here. Let the good fight begin.

It's those who don't make it to the gym floor or accept the clever, all-inclusive answer "Because, that's why" who have the big problem. Purpose has withered; it has become less than the need. Motivation has become clouded by the haze of the days. Inspiration, like withered fruit on a sunless tree, has lost its sweetness. Drive has stalled with the lack of direction. And there is little enthusiasm when the destination is unclear.

But wait, there's more. Miss one workout and we surely miss two and three and four. We get soft, weak, unhealthy, unkempt, undisciplined, unstructured, irritable, rude and ugly. We eat fast food, stock the fridge with beer, stay up late watching TV, lose our jobs and back the pickup into the neighbor's candy-apple red '65 Ford Cobra. What a mess. Those aluminum bodies cannot take the bumper of an unruly four-by-four SUV.

Stop. You're killin' me. I can't take it anymore.

Let's make a list of the enemies that attack our daily lives, bringing us down from the sky where we fly. We will set apart the assailants and devise counteractions to the common destructive force to all musclebuilders: lack of motivation.

Oh, boy, where do we begin? Remember, this is not an exercise to summarize the negatives and wallow in the pain; it is a sweep of the waste and trash that gathers around us over the years and needs to be attended. To see it is to know it, dumping what we can and keeping the remainder in a stinky pile by the workshed. Yeah, it's there, but it's out of the way. I don't smell anything, do you?

1) World weariness… This mean-faced, two-faced and two-fisted scoundrel has been a dark resident of the world since the day there were two or more inhabitants, a long, long time.

We are the chief contributors to its cause, along with thunder, lightning, wind, rain and fire. It's the economy, stupid... nothing that a stack of hundreds wouldn't fix. Not really; tell that to the mother of a kid who's lifeless after a high school shooting. Did we elect these politicians to manage our homeland or cause its implosion? They're a bunch of crooks and boneheads. And, by the way, what is the level of terrorist-alert this fine Friday morning? Black and blue? Sorry I'm late, Dear. Some man was threatening to throw his body onto the freeway unless we improve our highways, something about tax dollars and freedom of expression under a recent amendment to the Constitution. He's got a whole bunch of supporters standing in the middle of Route 1 chanting, "Man against traffic." And, no, I didn't get the job today. Three illegal immigrants from Columbia were there before me and were hired on the spot. Good thing I don't do drugs; they were passing them out to celebrate.

Another good thing — I belong to the gym down the street where the pump replaces the anger; the challenge under the iron overpowers the stupidity of lawmakers; the camaraderie on the floor makes up for the loss of time on the freeway and the muscle and might fights against crime, slime and grime. And that's the facts, Jax.

2) Injury and illness... It's the shoulder today, the lower back yesterday and I feel fatigue coming on with my runny nose. I train too hard when I train at all and, thus, overtrain, which stops me from continuing to train, so why bother? If it's not one thing, it's another.

There's the spirit: tough, undaunted and unstoppable. We know what the "C" stands for in your name, Courageous, not cowardly and complaining. If the hospital won't take you, go to the gym, that's what I always say. More healing, repairing, strengthening, energizing, immunizing and detoxifying takes place on the gym floor and in our heads than in most infirmaries. This has not been proven yet, but we're working on it.

Ask anyone who trains regularly: take a week off and everything hurts, you feel like you're gonna collapse and you want to bite people's heads off. Focus, learn from the pain, wear wraps, use ice, take ibuprophen occasionally and smile.

3) Sticking points and plateaus... Plateau is often a another word for impatience, sometimes immaturity and, perhaps, secret excuse. Building muscle and losing fat takes Time with a capital "T." That means many moons, Chief Wannabe, hard work, healthy sacrifice, joyful compromise and stick-to-it-tiveness. Where have these basic necessities gone?

A 20-something guy and gal stunned by their inability to accomplish their goals asked me for training and nutritional advice as I departed for home, gym bag in hand. I felt compassion for the wayward pair and gave them all the fair counsel two youngsters could absorb. As I left they confessed they hadn't been training all that long, two months. My eyes narrowed. What plateau does one encounter in two months? You can't make, invent, uncover or discover a plateau in two months. It's not physically possible. That's not enough time to gather enough dirt to construct a plateau.

If the door seems locked, try the key, try another entrance, crawl through the window, cut a hole in the roof or dig a tunnel under the floor. If those attempts fail, kick in the door or remove a wall. Use your logic, stir your imagination, revive your desire and realize your need. Do not submit to boredom, doubt or disappointment, ever, or you will be afflicted by the demons the rest of your life.

4) The home front... Our home is our castle and the wards and inhabitants of the castle — the family — must be strong, confident, rational and quick-minded to defend and keep its walls secure. Why do I think drinking beer and watching the WWF and MTV and snoozing on the couch do little to pre-serve and perpetuate the homefront? Avoidance of responsi-bilities and procrastination are on the top of the list of those persons who are failing and struggling in society today. The eat, live and be merry crowd will get fat, sluggish and die before their time. Paint that wall, fix that fence, save some money and forego the new SUV and the Mediterranean cruise to be paid for with a credit card, now and forevermore.

Go to the gym, young person, and take your loving spouse with you. What an uplifting diversion the gym experience is when you share it with a friend and recognize its amazing ben-efits and rewards. The gym builds, matures, beautifies, sus-tains, glorifies and adds years of quality to your life. And don't you think these appreciations are evident within the four walls of the house and home? When trials rise before you, so do your strengths.

5) Job and career... A tough one for sure, Boss. Who are we, where are we going, is this all there is, can I do better, is it worth it? The list of questions is long and confounding; it's presented early and is ever-present. If you don't like your job, your boss or the associates with whom you spend a third of your daily life, you're in a dark place, a pit. Sometimes the money explains the compromise, the benefits, the hours and the con-venience. Good enough. Hey, you say, at least I've got a job. Sterling response. We are an ever-hopeful bunch and you keep your eyes and ears open.

How about being your own boss, stepping up the ladder, going to school, taking a series of seminars? These aggressive moves take a man and woman of action, stamina and guts. Do you know where one builds action, stamina and guts? In the gym under the iron day after day, forever without fail, and without excuses or grumbling, that's where. It's true. I read a study somewhere and that's what it said, really.

The first thing a person does when he loses his job is quit the gym — when he needs it the most: positive input, uplifting distraction, confidence-building, back-building. Folks bored with work and school and play, they stop going to the gym — when they need it the most: restoring, revitalizing, disciplinary. Can't handle the boss, the employee loses interest in striving and forgets his workouts — when he needs them the most: de-stresses, provides an outlet for expression. Boom, zoom.

6) Relationships... This includes finding a mate, keeping a mate, divorce, courtship and marriage, bad boss, staff or partners, neighbors and friends and training partners and relatives. For some, the more the better; for others, the less the better or none whatsoever, and that goes for you, Bub. Here we make our way through the crowd with little invisible feelers extending from our hearts, minds and emotions. It's hard to distinguish a friend from a post sometimes, but we keep following the buzz. They come and go and when they go and you wish they hadn't, you wonder if it was you or they, and it can hurt more than fire to the flesh. The iron does not distinguish between friend and foe, but responds to the love we offer it. When the metal is dormant, it's you who needs the work. Never let it die.

7) The gym... Where musclebuilding takes place: crowded, funky, out-of-the-way, insufficiently equipped, wrong atmosphere and full of smudged mirrors and jerks. I hope that doesn't describe your local iron-and-steel watering hole. If it does, think garage, Olympic set, squat rack and a bench. The person who must work out can train in a dungeon, believe me. For the beginning trainees, the last impression they need is the most common scene they are introduced to across our fertile

104

pastures and fruited planes: hyped energy, endless stationary bikes and running and climbing machines in a dazzling florescent white convention-hall setting, lined with mirrors and occupied with gaily outfitted, but disillusioned hopefuls strutting in unison. Who are they and where do they come from?

Choose your gym wisely. Seek a clean iron refuge, a steel workplace, not a flashy cushioned playpen for adult toddlers. You can either get the job done with purpose and be certain, or fuss with colorful tinker toys, erector sets and building blocks till it's time to go bye-bye.

8) Personal resolutions... When the sum total of who you are comes under scrutiny and you are not entirely pleased with what you see, consider it a fair thing. Pride doth break our back and healing comes with humility. Caution: Should we hate ourselves, our motivation pours out like fresh water from a cup at the well. Yet, how can one so bright put aside his exercise? To amend the plight we need more time in the gym, not less. When we've lost direction and our place is not clear, rely on the work accomplished within our souls as we accomplish the work on our mighty and miraculous bodies. Time continues its fixed pace and we are all taken by surprise by the turn of a generation, dismay frequently in attendance. Train hard, eat right, care more and worry less... worry no more. About spiritual things: I don't know a Christian, a Muslim, a Buddhist or a Jew who isn't a better person when he works out and eats right. There'd be fewer battles, less drugs and less crime and more happy moms and dads if we all lifted weights and ate more protein... Fact of life.

9) Nutrition: Not enough protein, too much junk and sugar ... I think it's safe to say too many of us — more accurately, too many of those outside these pages — eat too much sugar and junk food and get fat, overload the system, upset hormonal balances, become irritable, hyperactive or depressed, distress the heart and capillaries, and, thus, advance disease, diminish energy, endurance and well-being, sex drive and sex appeal, and the motivation to lift weights. Replace the goop with fresh fruit, salads and vegetables, meat, fish, poultry and milk products, some whole grains and nuts and essential fatty acids (EFAs). Eat right and live long, live well.

10) Training uncertainty... Beg, borrow or rent a copy of *Brother Iron Sister Steel*, my earlier book, to eliminate this, the ninth contributor to the musclebuilder's lack of motivation.

Lack of motivation is for the birds, not the bombers.

Barrels, Anvils and Logs

Over the years, I claimed I would eventually reveal my Secret 14-Day Muscularizing Routine and Eating Plan.

I lied. There is no secret routine. The truth is there is no secret to muscularizing.

You eat lots of protein and train like crazy till the job is done. Not much more to it than that. What there is, you figure out along the way. Try it. Worse thing you can do, besides quitting, is thinking too much: researching, reading, studying, referring to the muscle mags and asking everyone else for advice. You are "it," Bomber. You and your self are the whole, the question and the answer, the problem and the solution, the challenge and the victor, the raw material and the finished product. Intellectualizing is exhausting and suffocating. You need oxygen and action. Got it? Get it.

Super. Now, that doesn't mean you can't talk things over with a friend, a tree stump or your pet. Mugsy, my cat, and I don't get into great detail, but we sort out the basics and encourage each other regularly. Review and encouragement, reflection and hope, observation and humor, assessment and adjustment, these are the essential tools of construction, the implements of development seldom at hand. Let's make them ever-ready.

A word of support can carry you over broken glass and burning embers. The other day a guy stood behind me as I squatted, and said, "You're looking good, man. Stay tight, two more reps, you can do it." I got four and a pump and burn like I was 21 and loaded with jungle carbs. Turns out the guy at my back was 13 and talking to his schoolmate at the next rack. I would have been embarrassed if I didn't feel so darn good.

When perplexed I remind myself that someone had to think this stuff up. Many hazy years ago some brute, probably, or a less-then-delicate woman with hairy legs, stood in silence and contemplated muscle and strength. How can I be more powerful and physically impressive, lift heavier barrels, anvils and logs and bend bigger spikes? Practice, train, perform and repeat. Start small and add weight and size to the objects of attention. Improvise stuff, devise and contrive weighted things to assist the musclebuilding and strength-building process: stones of different sizes, logs of various thickness, length and weight, graduating barrels filled with material of increasing density, assorted steel rails and axels with wheels on the ends.

The latter is a most interesting concept, worth developing. We'll call them barbells.

Pulling things is unlike pushing things and broadens the treatment of muscle and might. A rope over the back or around the waist or formed into a harness is attached to a wagon, empty at first and later loaded with men and women of like interest.

The passionate one-man beast-of-burden pulls with all his might till the wagon creaks forward and his body screams in wondrous pain as the whole affair reaches for its mark across a stretch of rutted dirt road. The occupants go for the ride of their lives and spectators line up to award the rope-bearing, sinewy marvel with cheers and laughter. What a grand feat.

How about this? Sitting on the ground with his feet braced facing the wagon and the rope in his grasp, Big Mac pulls the staggering load to him hand over hand. Or, a platform is constructed, a rope is dropped through a hole in its center and attached to a weighted object and lifted from above. Here's a simple one: The strongman hangs from an overhead beam and pulls himself upward till his chin touches the beam and lowers himself fully as many consecutive times as possible — call them a set of repetitions.

What I'm saying is this, sky buddies: This is not rocket science with mathematical formulas and equations requiring genius. It's not masterful techniques and intimidating processes. Nor is it inherent talents or accomplished skills. It's lifting weights — and eating good food — for Pete's sake. It's not voodoo and a witch's brew, black magic, smoke and mirrors. It's logic, good old common sense, and persistence. It's resourcefulness and guts. It's glorious hard work.

Relax and be confident. Don't stiffarm your training or place it coldly outside your life as if it were a bad-tempered junkyard dog or a simple-minded relative. Get comfortable with exercise, cozy with your training. Know it as you know a friend. We can love good friends, and find them maddening at times, but they are entirely too important to be neglected. So it is with the vigorous activity of exercise, the vital undertaking of fitness. A little of both sentiments, love and need, with an accent on appreciation and respect is quite an agreeable mix.

Every aspect of weight training, a most worthy venture, takes more time and work than most people think, much to their surprise and disappointment. After a month most aspirants feel beat up and cheated, toppling off the wagon and onto the pitted road below. The wagon bounces along with a hardy bunch still clinging to its sideboards, the journey a wild one and destination a seductive unknown. God bless them, and mercy on those who toppled and settled with yesterday's dust.

Among the selection of goals sought by the lifter, muscularity is possibly the classiest. Muscle mass is impressive, shape is envied and strength is everyone's prize. Yet, fine muscle definition carried with ease is hot like fire. Sinew visible through thin skin and crowned with faint veins conveys instant quickness, sudden power and boundless energy. Raw human life itself is seen in vivid action: rippling, separating, stretching and contracting; functioning, living and breathing. In man or woman, it's fascinating, captivating and alluring. I want some.

Believe it or not, when the urge to muscularize is overpowering, the first thing I do is reference my 101-book library and stacks of muscle magazines and start my thumb-through study. I run a search on my computer with any word that suggests raw, ripped muscles. After weeks of collecting material from 10,000 sources, I narrow the field of approach to 49, my favorite number. Of course, now I'm exhausted and could care less about… what was it again, rips, tears, cuts, shreds?

When that fails I perform the same routine that provides muscle mass, only I lighten the load by ten to twenty percent and increase the pace by the same. This is an estimation that is calculated through my sensory perception and never reaches hard copy. The exercises are the basics, and supersetting — one exercise followed by another that complements the first — is a key technique. Be prepared for volume in your routine, that is, lots of sets and reps, pumping and burning, as well as an exciting pace and panting, till you're conditioned by the enthusiastic method of operation and readied for its benefits.

Modern or new-age lifters might say, "The basics, supersetting and volume? You'll never build muscle that way. I read it somewhere. That's overtraining."

Yeah, well get over it. Unless you're one in 20 million (my own approximation) or you're looking for cute little teeny weeny, itsy bitsy muscles, you're going to require hard work and lots of it. I withdraw the second condition of the former statement; itsy bitsy muscles require hard work and lots of it, too. And if you're new at this stuff, maybe muscularity isn't in your immediate future. Good old-fashioned muscle of any description might be most acceptable... and agreeable. You're reading a chapter for another day in the life of your pursuits. Be of good cheer; the information is still useful.

Here's where learning to love your training comes in handy.

An early disclaimer: Beware of excessive aerobic exercise in your eagerness to achieve muscle hardness and separation. You might very well lose valuable muscle at the cost of losing bodyfat. I find nothing more frightening except maybe the boogieman. Consider high intensity interval training (HIIT) sessions of twelve to fifteen minutes, four days a week, on your off-days when possible.

You want to train each muscle group, directly or indirectly, two times a week over a four-day workout week. Don't be random in your routine, but allow yourself legitimate margin for exercise alterations where and when necessary.

Without being a wimp, if a series of tough workouts fatigue you, let a day go by so you can blast it the next day. If the insertions are tender in the biceps, change your standing barbell curl to thumbs-up curls or reverse curls or wrist curls; if the bench is killing your shoulders, go to dumbbells to avoid damage and allow relief and repair. When your legs are noodles, work the shoulders and arms and catch up with the legs the following day or so. Fit it all together with feel, instinct, logic and finesse — and responsibility.

Hit the abs and torso and lower back as a region three or four times a week with full-bore vigor, high reps, tight contractions and multi-set combinations one workout to the next. Vary the combinations of exercises to make the job interesting and certain, as the healthy condition of the region of muscles is vital and its toned appearance most appealing. Allow 15 to 20 minutes for the tough, worthwhile action, remembering the activity is aerobic and prepares the body for action. You'll beat the back pain and disability of midlife and old age. You'll stay strong.

Well, put down my landing gear, I've come to the end of the runway. Take advantage of the amazing days and the fine life we share.

Training Motivation, Intensity

As I sit with my head pressed against the blank computer screen while gripping the keyboard till my knuckles are white, those days when trying to formulate the substance of yet another stirring column with the aid of meditation practiced while hanging by my thumbs from a chinning bar under the house, and, yes, during the lonely midnight hours paging through old muscle magazines in search of inspiration and originality, I wonder to whom am I writing, who is it I'm trying to reach and who reads these desperate words squeezed from my parched brain.

Is it you? Then I'm encouraged and I'll write again; I'll write till I'm pale and bent. Worthy words, though they be reworked like clay in the potter's hand, the same true mud in another shape, another form, sometimes a cup, sometimes a bowl or serving dish, other times a pitcher or a decorative wall hanging of an imaginative abstract design. How about a life-size statue of me, upper body only, with my arms folded across my writhing pectoral muscles? Call it, "The Bomber."

In the absence of someting constructive to do, I assembled a loose list of musclebuilding types and present the collection to you. Please stand up when you recognize the type that most accurately describes you... at least raise your hand and say "here." Alright, just raise your hand. Okay, then, just sit there like a lump of meaningless clay. See if I care.

- Unassuming youngster who simply wants muscles and doesn't need psychoanalysis

- Totally new, never-touched-a-weight trainee, no longer a kid, needs a clue

- Returning trainee, lifted in high school (more or less) and recognizes the real need for fitness

- Overweight and needing weight loss and general conditioning

- Frivolous person looking for fun, friends and a date; muscle, might and health be darned

- Underweight and seeking muscle, mass and strength

- Athlete pursuing peak performance — strength, energy, endurance, speed

• Fit guy or gal — no longer a kid, yet a kid at heart — who trains regularly, has been bitten by the bug and wants to get into super shape: veins, abs and striations

• The hardcore lifter, been around and knows black from white, good from ugly, and wants what he or she can get, honorably

• The kid or no-longer-a-kid musclebuilder who wants it all now, as convincingly promised by the fakes, frauds and liars and marketeers, knows all the goofy ingredients and all the razor-ripping, cutting-edge techniques by name, thinks they're real and wants a final opinion as to which is best (that would be... fast, pain-less and cheap)

• The slick-dude type who's got a membership at Gold's and 24-Hour, one personal trainer (who says he's a former Mr. America from Brazil), two online training certificates — HPTA and RPTA (Huge Personal Trainer Association, Ripped Personal Trainer Association) — and once met Arnold at the Classic. Considers Frank Zane old-fashioned and the Bomber out of touch and can't help setting us straight

I think that covers it. You can sit down now, lower your hand... good. Thank you.

Whoever you are, whatever your specific needs might be, the basic requirements are the same. You must train hard, at-tentively, consistently and confidently. No matter what level you have achieved and what boundaries confront you, tough input is fundamental, absolutely imperative. It's the musclebuilding fact of life. The same is expected of your eating habits. They must be simply and wisely defined and toughly applied. Be tough.

Tough — anything that's tough sounds rough and agonizing, difficult and unappealing: tough neighborhood, tough exam, tough journey. They are not friendly; they do not suggest joy; they are, in fact, undesirable. This is not so in the application of "tough" to a workout or to the performer of such a workout. Tough is not dismal. Tough is very good, very cool, the embodiment of all that is strong and gutsy and exceptional. Tough is enviable and is to be embraced. A tough lifter faces a tough workout with a welcome chill, his head up and an unconscious correction of posture — it just happens. Tough is tough, a badge of honor. Anyone who grumbles about tough, is not. Remember that, bombers. Tough is reserved for the silent, enduring fighter.

Tough, like beauty, is in the eye of the beholder. What one perceives as tough is not tough to another. Beware of the jagged edges protruding from its nasty step-cousins. Be as tough as you like, tough in workout quality, volume performance and personal expectation, but not damaging, bitter, harsh or mean. Don't be cruel, don't be merciless. Be tough and merciful and take the time to understand the difference.

I'm cool. You cool? We're cool; we're tough.

Then there's intensity — intensity in physical exertion, in attitude and pursuit. The intensity factor rules, not things of learning so much as things of the heart and instincts, passions and mettle. Commit intensely. Desire intensely. Hope intensely. Focus intensely. Persist, push and pull hard, of course, but intensely pursue exercise understanding. The routines, the exercises, sets and reps are stacked up in a neat pile according to the needs of the athlete. Any bodybuilding primer for dummies will provide the necessary formulas to accomplish most degrees of development. They are not profound, complicated or exotic, nor need they be. They are embarrassingly simple and ordinary, original and essential. The stack is large for large advances and small for small advances. Common sense plus logic equals results. Master common sense, apply it intensely and you will master musclebuilding, good health and long life — and, I dare say, that list goes on and on.

I have observed on various gym floors various degrees of intensity in various weight trainers. Excluding the remarkably muscular men and women who have it by nature, the harder one exercises, the more one achieves. And the more one achieves, the more encouraged, inspired, fulfilled and happy one becomes. Training with intensity thus becomes a joy. I have also observed, apart from the champions, few train with the forced intensity or joyful intensity one must apply to progress. Their achievements thus are slow in coming, their joy and fulfillment is delayed. The delay of attainment and gratification is costly should they wander off before the magnificent experience of muscle and might graces them.

What exercises champions of today perform for building big arms, what regimens I apply to lose weight and get in shape or how Lee Haney gained muscle mass and power in the chest and shoulders are interesting discussions and help us in moving forward. Yet, we will find no new thing; the methods put forth don't require the application of complex formulas nor are they brilliant techniques unfolding. What we learn are things as familiar as one-syllable words, one plus one equals two and see Jane jump. The burly fellow by the water fountain in the shredded tank-top scratching his bottom, he's got it. It's easy.

Intensity defines one's achievement.

Intensity is a state of training performance. Seek it, locate and define it; research and study it as you apply it, determine the measure that is personally agreeable, desirable and lock on.

This is your target intensity as you focus on your workouts, your level of exercise output based on pressure and pain and your willingness to endure it. Embrace it and know it, understand it. It has the nature of a dear and dependable friend.

I suspect you'll want to regularly increase intensity's valuable effect. That is, you'll want to blast your workouts more and more for the fun and achievement of it. Blast on, bombers.

Some folks take intensity to outrageous levels. They vomit; they stagger and drop, they use smelling salts and rude outbursts to accompany their lifting madness. Their training becomes fodder for war stories to be boasted and circulated among the troops. They mount the injuries high, lower the quality of exercise performance and shorten their careers as lifters. They fall out of love and lose affection for the wholesome activity; fear, dread and hate replace the higher emotions they should have sought as they developed their training technique.

Others are frightened by intensity as if their muscles will certainly fall off their bodies and onto the gym floor should they apply the nasty force. Oh, my. What are we to do now? They greet pain as if it were a roaring lion, a crazed and clawing grizzly bear. Pain is as close to them as the North Star, as desirable as hemorrhoids. They flutter and flit about, the total iron on the pulley's weight stack barely a counterbalance to the handle swinging from the working end. They do seriously high reps with three-pound dumbbells and you find yourself nodding off to the hypnotic rhythm registering in your peripheral vision. Inspiration and aspiration are not among the motivators of this particular species of gym rat. Typically they carry on 20 minutes, as long as it takes to reach exhaustion, boredom or the lockerroom entry, whichever comes first.

Intensity comes in different shapes and sizes. Have you seen the whacky guy whose intensity is so great his eyes are like saucers upon entering the gym? He's fast-paced, red-faced and deep breathing with both arms clutching a bundle of rag-gedy gear, the sneakers dangling by knotted laces. His gym membership card's gripped in his bared teeth and to the person behind the counter he offers the moist plastic with a nudging action of his chin. Once on the exercise floor the intensity drains from his faint body and he practically falls asleep stretching on a mat, earphones in place. If anybody needs to apply training intensity it's this guy, a walking freaked-out danger zone. Hav-ing arrived and entered the gym doors is enough for one day.

Intensity often takes on the appearance of unfriendliness, sternness, anger or distress. This I know. It's not uncommon that the high-intensity trainee is a perfectionist, self-demand-ing, and loathes distraction. He's bad, which is, well, sort of good.

Intensify! I don't see any other way to get where you're going if you plan to get there. Review the possibilities, make your choice and suit yourself.

Thank heaven we are bombers, tough, intense and on tar-get. There's a time to glide and let the currents carry you along, and there's a time create some wind of your own, a storm if you must.

Cut loose and ride the horizons.

This is not a startling revelation to you and to me, but it's worth repeating to our neighbor: The best thing we can do in a continuing effort to enhance our apparently declining world is take control of our own lives, personally, individually. Forget war, crime and immorality for a minute and we notice we are surrounded by masses just poking along like life was a chore, the late shift, a bad habit or a dull pain and not a fragrant gift. Wake up, friends, wake up. We're broken, we need fixing and it's in our control. It's simple, yet it takes courage and work.

Can you hear me? It takes personal courage and it takes hard work.

I'm losing most of the population, I can tell. "Courage and hard work" do not ring a bell in the town square; they don't register on the scale of *Popular Daily Behavior* and I do not see them on today's list of *Currently Applied Qualities* in *Vogue Magazine*.

I can get downright mean when trying to rebuild society.

Bomb Squad Discourse

About today's fitness: Life on the gym floor is simple, our daily menu no big puzzle, and getting through a workout without tripping over our feet takes one mighty step at a time. What's the big deal? The ordinary guy and gal do it every day... poorly.

I know. I hear what I'm saying. I see what I'm writing and maybe I'm a cynic. Cynicism is a bone I love to chew on, but it's not the meat of my diet. It keeps me busy and it keeps my teeth sharp. There's marrow in those bones, calcium and some flavor, and the chewing engenders the production of healthy enzymes. I'm really a wild and optimistic musclehead whose irritating rants are compassionate pleas in disguise.

A word from the Bomb Squad:

About discipline: Regarded by many as a tyrant and by a blessed few as a magnificent force that causes, effects and directs, there is no doubt of its incredible power. It is an absolute in achievement and shapes the world by shaping the people. Sadly, the world's condition is also influenced by those dismal characters who reject the great power, cannot sustain its efforts or idly contain crevices as discipline passes them by. Should we embrace the steely energy and apply it to good, what a wonderful world this would be.

Long may the bombers, cultivating discipline's benefits and disposed to its favors, continue their contribution to a finer world.

Each of us has considerable built-in discipline (instinctive or survival discipline) to control many of our assets and faculties. We arise each morning, wash our faces, brush our teeth, comb the hairs on our heads and go about preparing breakfast before it's off to work. Discipline in action; it's cool, it works and we have it. We have this untapped personal control in sufficient supply to effect changes, improvements and advances in our precious lives. We simply need to add fuel, oxygen and motion and a little daily practice. Like watering a flower taking root in a crack of soil in the tarmac of life's vast, encroaching parking lot, don't let it die. We need all the flowers we can get.

I just find it hard to agree with new-age thinkers who declare that a person can achieve anything he wants to — play a piano solo in the New York Philharmonic, scale Mount Everest in his wheelchair, gain financial independence and personal happiness in the global real estate market — if he simply tries hard enough. "You can do anything you want to do if you put your mind to it, if you believe and don't doubt," say the leaders of popular win-win seminars and commercials selling waterfront properties in Nevada and infomercials hustling internet business software. Walk on fire? I don't think so. This success stuff turns nice people into scrappy wolves or disappointed lambs.

Discipline is not owned by repeating mantras, reading a book, watching a video or following a formula. Discipline is founded in need and desire and developed in deed. Discipline is yours. You want something, if you can't buy it or steal it, you must work for it. The more you want and need it, the harder you try to get it. The wanting and needing — the working, trying and getting — combine and eventually present discipline. Great or small, the stoic quality is a benefactor assuring that you become a better person, more complete and capable and aware, as you pursue your healthy and humble goal giving it your very best shot. The heart and soul and mind grow strong in the body while on the gym floor knocking out the sets after a day's hard work and plentiful supply of protein... and sufficient discipline.

And it deserves nobler applications than egocentric gain. Not everyone can bench 450, have nineteen-inch arms or wear a bathing suit like a model. This does not limit your achievement of the treasures discipline affords. Keep your head on your shoulders and your deltoids will grow.

About laziness: A hideous trait that leads to dullness and poverty and is inherited by the simple and practiced by the ignorant; there is no doubt of its corruptible weakness. Left to its inertia, little is accomplished and not much is enjoyed. Fulfillment has no chance in the lax and sluggish individual. He gets by.

The lazy guy or gal has enough discipline to accommodate the chores and hygiene and bare responsibilities of the day, but applies the barest energy to things of achievement and acclaim. The architects of the TV and remote, fast food and frozen dinners and microwave, the baggy pants and the muu-muus planted today's crop of corn. Like fields of droopy stalks rattling in the breeze, the harvest is plentiful, but the produce dry and hollow.

The lazy add nothing to the community or neighborhood. They provide no support. They are an encumbrance, a nuisance. They sit on the leg extension and read *People Magazine*.

About motivation: the key that starts the engine that impels us forward; unlocks the door and opens it wider; releases the integral energy that builds on itself like the atom. Without it accomplishments are accidental and success a chance occurrence. The reason we do things is often disguised in the tasteless task of daily living. With barely enough flavor to get us through the day, we urgently need seasonings to greet another morning's sun.

Purpose is accompanied by at least a teaspoon of heated passion and regular portions of savory fulfillment; they are treats and ongoing nourishment. Life with sweet motivation, inspiration and enthusiasm is a feast. Without them we live on bread and water. Might I interest you in a thick slice of roast prime rib of beef, a juicy Thanksgiving turkey leg or a fresh Crab Louie salad? Help yourself. Get ripped.

About patience: The art of waiting, the skill of working dauntlessly and hard while nothing appears to get done, the comfort found in hopefulness day after day, I suggest practice, practice and more practice till the cows come home and the roosters cackle. You can't stare at a pot and expect the water to boil without scorching your forehead on the steam. There's water in the pot and fire under it, right? Good. Hang back, stay cool and attend the sights and sounds of life around you. Just don't let the fire go out and the water evaporate. Get out the tea and cups and biscuits. We'll have a party.

Patience and time are juggled by the same clown. Time is not the problem; it's our concept of it. Life is a continuum interrupted by manmade units separating the past from the future. The clock has its benefits, but mostly serves to capture our minds in seconds, minutes and days, weeks, months and years, always counting, always watching... tic, tic, tic. Is that the way to build big muscles and a lean figure, lose bodyfat and set a personal record — from inside false compartments struggling to get out?

The stress of impatience squeezes the life out of time. It makes the moment unknowable and the present unbearable. We fret, we hurry, we become discouraged and we almost quit. Patience comes hard, it comes slow and it comes at a heavy price. Patience is tough and revives just as frustration prepares to wrestle us to the cold, dirty ground. We're back on our feet crouched and ready, a new level of fortitude in our command. Thank God for perseverance — the perseverance of bombers.

We are enduring, as the continuum stretches on. Impatience plus practice plus time equals fortitude, the first cousin of patience... once a stranger, now a friend. And we need all the friends we can get.

About perseverance: the long-lasting forever necessary to achieve, that familiar attribute set deep in the mind of the committed, motivated, patient and disciplined, the quality of the lithe racehorse never giving up, whether it wins or shows up last at the finish line. With perseverance you cannot lose. You stick to it or roll over, your breath no longer leaving a cloud on the mirror. Perseverance can be hard pushing and mean or a gentle effort, kind in its application, but always it is unceasing, positive in action and never falls short of finishing its work. About perseverance, it is undying.

Next time you work out, consider the five bombs we tossed around today. What role do they play in your training and how on the scale of one to ten do you score? Ten is perfect.

I figure we all know how to train — a curl is a curl, a squat is a squat, a shrug and so on... sets and reps, eat some tuna, drink some water. It's the DLMPP (Discipline, Laziness, Motivation, Patience, Perseverance) that gives us a run for the money. You get those right and everything else falls into place.

There you have my secret tip to building a lean sinewy body, bombers. Now let's practice individual and team formations — imaginative routines with renewed commitment and energy. Where craft value is lacking (perhaps an older model in need of reconditioning) we can proceed with resourcefulness, common sense and old-fashioned pain.

Breaking the Mold

Not every workout has to be a knockdown, drag-out battle. I'm all for blasting it and drawing blood, but sometimes it's just plain good to go to the gym and roll around on your back like a playful dog.

On those curious days when the old mutt in me — puppy, actually — comes yapping to the foreground all paws and no restraint, either because I'm way ahead of the game or so far behind it doesn't really matter, I let myself go and follow my tail. The results are always the same: a good time accompanied by relief, learning and growth. Oddly, the workouts are equally intense and unrelenting as the prescribed regimens; that I don't anticipate them, that they are spontaneous, the real deal and not a repeat performance, gives the execution of the movements freshness and the training a sense of adventure.

How long has it been since you associated freshness and adventure with your workouts?

I'm a proponent of sticking to a workout scheme for six weeks to achieve the maximum results it can afford. Too little time with one plan and you don't dig in deeply enough to excavate its densest ore; you don't overload the muscles repetitively enough with might and discovery to send the message to the brain that you need more powerful cellular structure, more rippling muscle to accommodate the consistently applied workload — you need the muscles to grow. Nevertheless, a tail-wagging diversion is often what's necessary to put some bark in the routine and bite in the workouts. Sit, stay, roll over... good doggie.

You get bored regularly? Tough. Keep digging!

Some people talk about surprising the muscles with new routines. Whoopee. What's this, a birthday party at the Pizza Hut? You've got to pound size and density and shape into your muscular system. That's when they and their possessor are their happiest, most content. Surprise your neighborhood in the summer by training like an animal in spring.

There are those who proclaim intense, steady, super-slow repetitions for maximum muscle intensity, something bordering on isometrics and dynamic tension with a twist of language suggesting it's the cutting-edge method. Where has the motion gone, the action, the excitement, the circulation of oxygen and blood and nutrients, the expression and revelry? Put me under an Olympic bar for ten minutes while I do six reps and I'll implode. Do it on a regular basis and you as an aspiring musclebuilder will last three days to three weeks. Don't listen to me. I'm just hypered, old-fashioned and narrow-minded.

"Short workouts of forty-five minutes, three times a week are the outer limits for the most efficient muscle and strength growth."

This theory is getting a lot of play from some wise guys who fear the demons of catabolism and don't really understand how anybody could want to go to the gym and get huge or ripped or strong and healthy. In forty-five minutes a good natural bodybuilder carrying any muscular size is just getting warmed up and inspired. You want time to fly? Throw the clock out the window. Zoom, zoom. You want to grow? You've got to do some saturating and penetrating and exploding. Boom, boom.

One workout a week per bodypart for beginner and advanced bodybuilders is a recent rule put forth by the big guys who hang out on the corner near Payless Drugs. Makes sense as long as you're intertwining and blending and overlapping exercises in such a brilliant way that every bodypart is receiving its necessary twice weekly blessing and bombing after all.

Don't be stingy. Don't be cowardly. Don't be lazy. Don't be dumb. Be generous and be wise. Use your common sense and train hard and efficiently, with good order, crisp pace, absolute focus, intelligence and zeal. Stop listening to the noisy voices out there that confuse you with the latest ingredient, methodology, holistic adventure, scheme, gadget, scam or whatever.

Look in the mirror and be that person you see, your best friend. Give him or her credit for inner knowledge and understanding. Learn the very simple basics in exercise and nutrition and practice and apply them happily and with confidence. Now you are on your way, not their way. You'll learn and you'll grow as the days go by under your tender-loving care. Stand and be strong.

I know the gym and training and good nutrition are important to you. Your health and well-being and body comfort are necessary and you don't want to make them your god or your worship. My gym is full of good folks who just love to mingle and stimulate and break up their day. It's healthy, productive and freeing. The one-hour expression refreshes the spirit, renews the body and inspires the mind. The gym is a refuge and fueling station, bombing and blasting excluded. It's a place and time to coax the muscles and fill the lungs and bloodstream with oxygen and goodness. Eyes toward the skies, you grab, lift, push and pull the iron, engage the cables and pulleys and make the back work. The moments are yours, well lived and valuable.

Jay who? Periodization when? Androstendione what? That's what I say, that's what I like to hear. Keep training, never doubt and turn up the volume if you get the urge. Forget the news, life is good.

Down the Highway and on My Mind

It's been a long day and you feel pummeled. Not everything went as planned — come to think of it, nothing went as planned — and you grope for hope. You check your attitude as you buckle your seatbelt, refusing to submit to the trivialities of the workday. You remind yourself that your strength of character is reflected in your behavior under minor stress; good days are around the bend and things could be a lot worse — the routines of the mind to assist in your transition from rattled to relaxed.

The key slides into the ignition and cranks over the engine with a zoom signaling that part one of the day is over, no small feat. You feel free for a moment, the tether that binds given slack by the forward lurch of your vehicle, your private space capsule that moves you to your next task site or playground, objective or challenge. These small interludes provide time to collect your thoughts, visualize your day, converse with yourself and otherwise glean the chaff from the wheat.

What's your plan, where are you headed and what's on your mind as the first mile rolls away? I'm expecting a large number of folk across the fields and fences and cities are headed home to couch, fridge and TV. Good to kick off the shoes and let the hair down. Some need to take a deep breath and wrestle a second job or a long list of unending chores. A moist handful, of course, move quickly and without obstruction to strategically placed watering holes. Whatever it takes, I guess, to move the pieces across the board.

But wait a minute. There exists a rare breed unaccounted for in the above collection of characters. In a certain place where the sun shines and the air is full of oxygen, the navigator of his or her vehicle steers clear of the traffic and heads to the gym. Thoughts are on grander things, life, love and the pursuit of happiness; or, as interpreted on another level, discipline, patience and the pursuit of pain. Whatever it takes, I'm certain, to improve the worth of life.

You know this singular sort whose habits do not resemble those of his neighbor. His countenance glows, his gait is sure and determination marks his actions.

That rare breed is you.

And the time and place you spend before entering the gym, be it on Main Street or in the garage, are rare as well. As the gym is a refuge and an area for productive work, so is the mind in preparation of a solid, bold and mighty workout. A powerful workout is established in one's head before entering the inner sanctum of the gym walls.

Be prepared!

Compromise, sacrifice, long-suffering and discomfort, no one said the task was easy and no one knows but the one who performs it. The groundwork begins in the mind, is effected in the body, transferred to the gym floor and finally to the iron where it is consummated by the fortitude, courage and heart of the pursuer.

That doesn't mean we don't love it — even when we hate it we love it. How can you hate that which is so wonderful and beneficial and, more often than not, fun and fulfilling?

Beware! "Self-centeredness and self-gratification are great deceivers," a ragged sage once said, "and we are the deceived." We reach for pleasure and relief, and grasp neglect and ruin instead.

I believe in giving each dimension of our life its due attention. We are wise not to be dominated by any one area of our lives to the neglect of another. Easily said, but great effort and discipline must be applied to achieve the balance. I've been known to fail, and not on rare occasions.

Nevertheless, sufficient workout forethought is fortifying and bright. Anticipating your training with a brief yet energetic review of its benefits — health and strength, the euphoric afterglow, the mental and physical purge, the admirable steps toward achieving goals, the personal investment in goodness and right — and a positive overview of your exercise scheme are all you need to fill your mind. Fill the mind with these magnificent thoughts and there is no room for the ugly twins, doubt and apathy.

Of course, the well-organized, efficient and successful person makes sure his energy and musclebuilding stores are supplied in advance. Adequate food and water must be part of the simple plan. That clear plastic bottle topped with cool water and a timely protein drink make the difference in superior mind and body performance.

So simple, so smart, so effective.

Stopping by the gym on the way home for a quick blast is admirable — in this day and age it is remarkable. But to be profitable and long lasting, a workout must be more or it will become less. As you must not let training or thinking about it dominate your life, so is it unwise to squeeze it in like a wedge of lemon in a cup of tea. Unfold a list of your top ten priorities and you'll find that exercising for your health is among the top five, and not a cozy cup of Constant Comment.

90 minutes, four days a week is your contribution, from the time you park your car to the time you pull away refreshed. Diligent work in the focused yet unrushed minutes between defines the physical investment. The rest of the week and the rest of your life are yours to give to your neighbor freely and generously.

Not that good things, mind you, don't take place without psychological and intellectual preparations. I rely heavily on the unseen work of the subconscious.

The gym is down the highway and on my mind. I'm home and though it's the weekend, I'll probably check in and, as long as I'm surrounded by weights, hit a decent workout. These unscheduled training sessions often turn out to be some of the best. I'm drawn to the iron by desire, not obligation. I don't have to lift, I want to. There's no pressure, no rush, no ground lost, no ground to make up, just the playground where time floats rather than flies by or drags on. And so it goes with physical preparation and mental psyche. They happen.

So, Draper. What do you want to do, what stirs you, what would you like to perfect or investigate, create or devise? The field is open and letting the workout evolve is a release that can be most instructive. Sufficient spontaneity is needed to provide freedom in your training without allowing it to become random and loose and unproductive in the long term. Here you may wallow in your favorite exercise combinations, try a personal best, switch to high repetitions for a pump and burn and the experience, or you might exact a dumbbell movement to work that part of your deltoid no standard exercise ever has. Hmm... a little creativity and thinking on one's feet go a long way to add to one's personal trust and training maturity.

Invention rings a bell, loud and clear.

Here's what I did the other day when time was on my side and I lived life as if it was mine and not the possession of the tyrant of urgency, the demon of conformity or the brute of convention.

I grasped the iron and proceeded to pick it up, push it and pull it. Hold on... it gets more interesting; I lift it and lower it, raise, press and extend it, all the time planning to swing it while contracting and isolating it. Do you get the picture? I'm hoisting, straining and laboriously maneuvering. I shove and thrust with might. Plates are flying. My heart is throbbing, I'm wet with sweat and I gasp for air. I'm hot now. Under the heavy metal I drive it away from my chest, over the metal I tug it to my shoulders and beneath the cumbersome weight I force it upward with my legs. Lost in spontaneity and revelry, I grab a pair of ungainly dumbbells and walk — rather, clomp — around the gym as if on a mission. I wind down after four breathless, staggering circuits about the equipment-strewn floor, and, finally, collapse.

You know when you're done 'cuz you fall off the bench and whimper as unimpressed, insensitive co-trainers step over you, nudge you with a foot and suggest you drag your sorry body under the dumbbell rack and out of the way.

Don't whimper, bombers. Sign of weakness.

Be thankful. The best seasons for flying high and fast are here. Hold on to the days and don't let go. Your training is an ongoing mission, every challenge a reward. When asked what defeat is, you'll answer, "I don't know."

God's speed, brothers and sisters.

Eat, Train and Be Happy

Good day, Sunshine, Mr. or Mrs. Newcomer. Aren't you glad you're working out, watching your diet and getting in shape? The tough job is over, partners. Confronting, starting and persisting compose the rockiest stretch of any exercise venture, like pushing a wheelbarrow of mud up Empire Grade. Training familiarity, investment and return level the ground before you. The way is clear. You need only to continue, submitting to no tempting distraction, contrived obligation, petty discomfort or other unpardonable excuse. You know how it goes: a day off leads to one more and then another. Don't play the game or in a single snooze on the couch you'll need to start all over again. Ugh. What a revolting predicament that is.

I offer you young musclemakers today's change-of-pace routine to spark your interest and startle the body: Perform twenty crunches followed by ten leg raises followed by ten deep-knee bends. The exercises are executed with a focus on form and sound pace. Three cycles with a short pause between each series are sufficient, though four is very cool and more repetitions for the more enduring are dandy. Ease into this ambitious warm-up applying your might as you build up momentum. The harder you work, the greater the return. You're stretching and contracting a lot of muscle and the heart and lungs are pumping. Life is good.

Next, with your feet placed firmly in a shoulder-width stance, crouch over a pair of light dumbbells as they lay on the floor before you. Apply a convincing grip, stand up and raise the dumbbells in one continuous motion to the shoulders, pause and press to an overhead position. Congratulations. You've just completed one rep of the dumbbell clean and press, a most significant and productive exercise. Slowly and attentively, reverse the movement and return the weights to their starting position. Repeat for a total of 8 to 10 repetitions. Three sets with ninety seconds rest between sets will serve you well. This gutsy original exercise is regaining its popularity (trendy lifters find it too tough) due to its systemic action; the entire body is involved in its execution resulting in the development of a network of muscle, practical strength, cardio-respiratory efficiency and functional skill. A golden exercise worth practicing, perfecting and framing. Tough is good.

Not to change the subject, but have you been eating your protein lately? Muscles are made of protein, you know. I agree with those docs who declare that no adult should ingest less than one hundred grams of the precious ingredient no matter how petite they are. Unless you have a pre-existing kidney or liver ailment, extra gobs of the stuff are not going to hurt you. Au contraire. As well as being the prime ingredient of muscle tissue, protein is a superior source of energy, unlikely to add fat anywhere. Excuse me. Espousing such propaganda get can a person in trouble — strong and muscular, but in trouble. As a convicted, life-long bodybuilder, I feel compelled to toot my horn for protein. Sugar is a stinker. Oops.

Across the nations most people are eating too much and eating the wrong foods. And very few are truly exercising. Hence, our roundness and sluggishness. Diet trends have us embracing carbohydrates, scorning fat and dabbling in protein. We need to be careful. Research groups under private grants telling half-truths to satisfy the interests of their wealthy sponsors — those corporations advertising the junk we eat — are perpetuating the misinformation we receive about nutrition. Hey, we're getting fat on politics. At least we'll never starve.

Good nutrition, like good training, is simple — learn the basics and practice them consistently. A little knowledge and a lot of discipline is the secret. Apply yourself diligently; look ahead, don't look back and don't look for shortcuts. There simply aren't any.

Health and fitness have climbed to the top of our popularity list and have become big business. As you've noticed, there's a gym on every corner and a glut of diet and bodybuilding formulas to pack on muscle and burn off fat.

Competition is fierce, the promises are bizarre and we're all confused, suspicious and eventually numb. We have on hand a zillion too many ways to diet, feed ourselves and live our lives for fitness. Think of these proportions — 40/30/30 — as percentage of protein to carbs to fat, and forget the rest.

Pssst… sugar is trouble, certain fats are essential and protein is, well, not to be worshipped but mildly adored. Eat smaller, balanced meals more frequently and mind your portion size. Don't forget your vitamin and mineral supplements and drink lots of water.

Discounting laziness, lack of ambition, irresponsibility and other ignoble disabilities, only one enemy stands in your way: doubt, a deception also known as negativity, misperception, suspicion and poor attitude.

We win not by luck or brilliance but through trust and confidence and persistent positive performance.

Welcome Time and He Loosens His Grip

The time has come to open the door and walk through. Youth isn't exactly ancient history, but it and the dust around it has settled in the past. Nod and toss a mock salute. Adios, Amigo. What youth didn't do for you, you must do now... pick up the pieces and put them together. That's why this day you stand beyond the door and on the gym floor. Say goodbye to the child, but be sure to take the kid with you.

The men or women who over the years and by accident or design built a foundation of muscle, fed themselves decently and treated their bodies fairly are rare and far ahead of the maddening crowd. They can step into a training program and proceed without the turmoil of emotions and toil of mind needed to focus and aspire.

Those sterling characters who started their robust fitness venture years ago and have persevered are aware of the precarious twists in the road ahead. They are even fewer, more accomplished and will not be thrown off course.

The few who gather in a tight circle around the piles of iron and steel, belts and wraps dangling from their strong grips, access the hairpin curve that edges the heights of the mountain they've climbed for so many years, they lead where no one has led before. Tilted heads studying, narrowed eyes focusing and knitted brows concentrating, they resourcefully improvise the next uncertain move. Stoic grins crowd their faces.

There's a smart way to go for each of us, depending on our fitness level, experience, constitution, health, means and available time. Here are some non-technical generalizations about aging based on my limited observations:

• Needless to say, the timeless teens and the 20-some fly high, far and fast. They are not, however, invincible; they strain and they break, they overtrain and complain. Age… it begins.

• The terrific 30-some grow, muscularize, further perfect shape and tone, and they gather and apply wisdom. Injuries and plateaus are responsible for the lattermost hard-earned accomplishments. Risk taking, heavy weights and mean persistence do their job, yet take their toll on the hardcore. Growing up and growing older… it continues.

• 40-some, frivolous and frantic, provides a stretch of positive growth for the trainee who didn't ignore his responsibility to fitness for a regretful length of time — the longer out of the loop, the bigger the penalty. The slightly abused or negligent pick up where they left off after dutifully and painfully re-establishing their parameters. Strength, muscle size and definition can be achieved by the tough, perceptive and determined, given time, and time moves on.

• The overused over-40 can do wonders to restore his or her health and well-being, control bodyweight, improve energy, strengthen the back and flatten the stomach. Self-esteem is added to the bargain. There's no time or effort to waste... today or ever again.

• The early 50s rock on as you suspiciously glance over your shoulder. A ding here and a ding there become more frequent and last a little longer and cause more concern. Human nature, I guess. To push or not to push, that is the question. We hesitate briefly, yet we don't stall and we don't fall apart. Caution is coolish... fear is foolish. We're hanging in there, mister and sister, as we head for 60. Very becoming.

• The 60s are where I draw a temporary line... it's as far as I've gotten and I'm all eyes and ears. It seems the curiosity and care I integrated and the wisdom I collected during the downside of the 50s have given me a head start on the big Six-Oh. I'm on an ascent that I hope and trust isn't a rare and isolated phase or a fluke. I'm stronger, healthier and fitter than I was five years ago. Not that long ago I had the gym to myself 'cuz it was a holiday. I trained casually with the floor empty, the sounds off and the lights low. I squatted 440 and deadlifted 500. No big deal and I ain't braggin,' but it indicates reasonably sound condition.

At any age under any circumstances, exercise and eating right will support the body, mind and spirit of every participant. The younger you start, the better the foundations. The longer you continue, the more durable the structure. The later you start, the more dramatic the life-sustaining renovations you experience. Never to have exercised with at least moderate passion is to have somehow withheld opportunity and dimension from your life. It's never too late to start.

Okay, already. What do we do?

The largest group of less-fortunates is the once-in-shape, now-out-of-shape, over-40-yet-not-100, back-in-the-gym, wondering-what-to-do bunch. What they must do is… well… start — get the immovable object in motion and keep it in motion despite all imaginary and real obstacles. This demands desire, commitment and guts. If these can't be arranged, it's back to the TV or job or refrigerator with their expanding britches and narrowing arteries and diminishing muscles and failing self-image. Face the facts, consider the consequences and hop in the pool; the water is fine. Exercise, eat right and be happy.

Wow. Aren't you glad you're past that stage? To those who are not, I usually say something like this:

What must be done? Exercise vigorously three days a week with the weights, and throw in some aerobics between workouts. It's wonderful, exhilarating and joyful. It's a challenge: a challenge that restores the body and revives the soul and regulates the emotions. What have you got against challenge? Too hard, too much trouble, no time, no interest, no courage, no confidence… exactly what is it? And about eating right, can we put some order in the menu, increase the meal frequency, add some protein and lower the sugars? Can we dump the junk and add living food packed with goodness? Can we apply discipline and satisfy our body's needs and not our cravings?

Absolutely. It takes time to rethink exercise and diet and embrace them for the rewards and benefits they offer, and the downright fun and fulfillment that accompanies action and control.

Has it been awhile? To the vast group of deconditioned I say this: Take heart and start walking. Over the weeks, add mild jogging to your walking and do ten minutes of crunches and leg raises at some specific time during the day — before dinner, before breakfast). Start planning to expand your exercise to the gym floor. A good gym can be a refuge, a rewarding diversion, a place of redemption and that bracing, long-absent challenge you need for fulfillment. Without these we wilt.

Once in the gym (and please don't put it off... see you there) do a little aerobics for warm-up, some crunches and leg raises for midsection and one basic exercise recalled from your past experience for each muscle group, two sets times 10 repetitions.

Three whole-body workouts, three alternate days a week for the first month as you practice, concentrate on the task at hand and the muscles at work, observe your surroundings, smile, nod and be extraordinarily happy. You are an extraordinary person applying quaking courage, reluctant responsibility and staggering persistence. These, too, are about to flourish and thrive.

Curious: What needs to be said about the technicalities of the workouts (sets, reps, exercises and combinations) is just... so technical. Workouts are workouts, mixed and matched to people, situations, circumstances, genetics, injuries, the past, the present and the future, moods, attitudes, doubts, conclusions, chemistry and character. What we think about and talk about between the lines is where the real questions and answers are exchanged.

Men and women, you are building all the main muscles throughout your body for balance, efficiency, health, strength and appearance. And today, what works for him works for her. As the climb continues, the course will change, but not much. That's another matter. For now don't wander from the basics and don't expect miracles beyond the one that you are experiencing. Enjoy yourself and continue to be hopeful and positive — the perfect environment for musclebuilding, health and long life.

There are more specific categories of training and aging, but let's give Old Man Time a break and stir up trouble in another neighborhood… another corner of the big blue sky.

I'm into some serious dive-bombing and zero-gravity stalls, testing the integrity of the wings and will.

Training Attitude: Sunshine on a Rainy Day

Good or bad, which one will it be?

Ah, the sweet fragrance of contentment. Life is good. We have choices. We're in control. We can pause on an elevated knoll, point in the direction of our goals and continue our venturesome journeys. There, that sunlit perch beyond the rocky plateau, a worthy destination within the capacity of our legs. We'll keep the pace, throw in a skip and a jump and be there before the day's end. What's the rush? After all, we can play along the way. Obstacles are only players on the field to outwit and out-maneuver as we move toward our goals.

Oh, the tyranny of frustration is brutal and ever-present. Life is cruel. The winds of doubt blow us about. Injury, illness and misbehavior crawl up our pant legs. With squinted eyes an unsure place somewhere on the far side of the misty glade is considered and measured. Looks near, but so does the moon in the early autumn twilight. Can't stay here with sloping shoulders, unsteady legs and a substantial backside to match an overhanging gut. But, what if we get lost or meet a hungry bear or slip off the hillside? Try and fail, try and fail.

Try, fail and quit is the manner of losers; try, fail and grow is the way of the strong.

I feel like a relic as I walk onto the gym floor. It's wet outside, daylight has faded to a foggy gray-black and it's not yet 5:00 o'clock. A threadbare song by Smashing Pumpkins is wheezing in the background making the weights look bigger, harder, colder and heavier than ever before. It's a lonely space. Few people are inspired to gnaw on the iron, tug on the cables and send voluntary nerve signals through the central nervous system to contract and extend their muscles. The equipment is still and unmanned. How tiresome, how inane. I'm hungry… no, I'm not. My body aches… no, it doesn't. I'm sleepy… I'm not sleepy.

I look for a corner and pull up a bench. My prolific gear, the straps and belts that hold me together, falls to the floor with a jangling thud. The water bottle is uncapped, upended and I guzzle for strength, courage and purpose… here and now. Overly ambitious, the cold and wet liquid escapes my mouth and washes down my face and the front of my t-shirt. Go ahead, ya mutt; wipe your mouth with the back of your hand like a slob. Who cares? Instinctively, I do.

I feel old and catch myself slouching. This will not do. I have an image — we all do — before myself and others and immediately reset my posture and gracefully undo all the evidence of a sorry old man, sort out the tools of my sport, take another pull on the H_2O — this time with vigor and purpose — throw back my shoulders and thoughtfully rub rosin on hands as if eager to lift. Stand back, lackeys. He's alive.

The Bomber taxis over to the Smith Press and arranges an incline bench in a unique fashion at a special angle, with the distance between the bar and the apex of the seat exactly seven inches. Who knows why? I assume the appropriate position and contemplate the punk condition of my attitude.

This isn't new. In fact my experience with lifting weights and the blues goes back as long as I can remember. About the third time I rolled them out from under my bed came the first confrontation with resistance. They looked less interesting and less important than they did the week before when I purchased the rusting heap from my neighbor, Johnny, the milkman. What a deal. For five bucks I was permitted to go behind the furnace in his basement, gather the misplaced ninety pounds of pig iron, drag it out and carry it home. I should have known then the thrill before me. I was weighing about sixty.

Something inside my gut said I had to lift the weights whether I wanted to or not. It was like going to school. You didn't go to school when you wanted to. (Ha, I'd never have gone to school were that the deal). You went or you didn't learn or grow, pass or gain folks' approval. In fact, disapproval from my parents was large and painful. No way did I skip classes or fail my grades and live to tell the tale. So it was with me and lifting the iron. It had to be done.

By time I was 17, I'd won and lost the battle of workouts more than I could count and was beginning to figure it out. You work out, you feel great. You don't work out, you feel like crap ('cuz me, Senora). You lift, you grow. You don't lift, you get soft and scrawny, like… overnight. The choice is yours. Some choice. Didn't seem fair then, doesn't seem fair now.

Eventually, I chose sides and determined that the correct path for this nutcase was to train as if there was no choice, since there really wasn't. I chewed on the line and sinker for years and finally got hooked. Weight training became a habit.

That didn't mean I automatically entered the gym without occasionally staring off and wondering what it would be like to simply walk away and come back when I felt like it. The moments were recurring and brief, like flashes of a strobe light, or, more accurately, jolts of electricity from a stun gun.

I lifted, I grew. I lifted, I felt great. I lifted, I grew older. Sometime around 40, after years of lifting tons of iron with my body, an ounce of wisdom entered my mind. Exercise, and the right eating that accompanies it, is our duty. No. That's not wisdom. How arrogant of me to suggest it. That is a fact. Wisdom is the presence of mind to practice the fact, to put into effect the plain, wholesome truth. Anything else is just dumb.

I got up and I strode to the dumbbell rack and latched onto a pair of hundreds and began to trek around the gym floor. They call them farmer walks because the movement simulates a farmer carrying heavy buckets of milk or grain around his fields. I call them marching around the gym floor with hundreds because it feels good and it's my duty.

There are times when you need to sit down on the old incline bench and talk things over with yourself. You don't have to make any sense. Nobody's listening. They're just staring. Sit up and look sharp, flex your lats and tense those tris. Fools 'em every time, bombers.

Lighten Up and Fly Right

Looking through bloodshot eyes and speaking in a scorched and breathless voice, I remind a co-trainer how grand it is to be lifting weights and that this is the best time of year for musclebuilding progress. We stand before the dumbbell racks that line the mirrored wall running the length of the gym. She nods while leaning on a pair of 20s for support, her posture and expression belying her message of agreement.

The sun is strong this afternoon, the air warm and the shift in the clock to daylight savings affords another hour to work and play. Time is freedom. Spirits rise, layers of clothing are removed and joints cooperate. Why, then, do I turn limp this time of the year and stagger in a mental, physical and attitude void, contradicting the obvious promise of the season?

Nobody said I'm alone. We expect to soar, instead we crash. Billy "Trees" walks past me as I precisely position an incline bench for some righteous abdominal work. He's grumbling 'cuz it's hot and he's sweaty and itchy and tired and it's Monday. "Poor baby," I offer my sympathy and encouragement, "This is the best time of year for musclebuilding progress, Bill. Time is freedom!" He glares, sawdust from trimming redwoods still in his ponytail. He'll be okay in a few sticky and bristling minutes… been there, been that way.

Water's a big seller at the juice bar and clear plastic bottles decorate the gym. Hand towels pass over damp foreheads and drape the equipment. Sweatshirts and Ts are tossed in corners and tanktops and croptops bob and weave about the benches, bars and racks. It's wonderfully warm, but the creatures are gasping.

The perfect blend of ingredients is present for unparalleled workouts and muscle response. We worship the first wave of warm weather, we rejoice in the sun and find relief in the extended daytime hours. The long, cold and dreary winter is over and we are liberated. No more dampness and chills, fewer aches and pains, less bulky gym wear and more exposure of skin, more pump and more burn. Here we come, tanned, toned and tapered.

Well, not exactly. The adaptable animal we are must adapt. The blood in our veins, the beat in our hearts and the air in our lungs need to adjust. Our hormones and digestive system are responding to seasonal changes in diet and patterns of eating and sleeping and extents and intensities of activity. We go through stress changes — a natural phase, AKA spring fever — as the days lengthen and the temperatures rise and our habits alter, ever so slighty.

What's wrong? Unsuspected fatigue might be misinterpreted as a mystery illness or depression or ennui. Unfamiliar with the phase, we try to overcome or override it with forced training tactics and grouchy days of insufferable workouts. "It's spring and I feel sprung," we say. Our appetite wanes, our muscles lose tone, we're tired, weak and looking soft. Great, just great! What happened to the pre-summer revival we've all been anticipating? Discouragement mounts, confidence slips.

This year, get it right. Don't panic and don't despair. It's spring, not the flu again or a triple by-pass or SARS or cooties. It's spring; stop and smell the flowers. It's spring; take a walk in the park, have an ice cream sandwich, go fishing or mow the lawn. It's the springtime six months ago we thought would never come, the long days, the cool nights with only the summer ahead when flying is high and landings are light and time drifts. Vacations and long weekends are in sight, barbecues and relaxed time with friends, no work, no responsibilities, lots of sleep and lots of food.

Of course, then the dilemma becomes laziness, missed workouts, misplaced discipline, zero energy, extinct self-esteem, lost muscle and gained fat. The summer will end on time — catching us offguard — and the winter will pounce on us mercilessly as always and we will long for the spring when everything is good and hopeful and wonderful and you will hear me say, "This is the best time of year for musclebuilding progress. Time is freedom!"

Stay cool, bombers. Be flexible and adapt. Lighten up and fly right.

By the person who trains hard, much is accomplished. The person who trains lightly is better off than the person who doesn't train at all.

If a man or woman exercises, the exercise should be of sufficient effort and thought to achieve its valuable benefits: health and long life, strength of character and strength of back.

If one trains with extraordinary delight, passion and desire, if he or she is committed, dauntless and absolutely wonderful, he or she is revered as a bomber the world over.

Soar, fly high and scan the horizons. Life above the earth's surface has its ecstatic moments. Landing is fun also.

Just Another Day

I'm about to leave for the gym. It's a sunny day, Saturday, one you might call perfect; low 70s, light breeze and no humidity. There are things I could do other than work out with the weights within the gym walls — more appealing and exciting, perhaps — yet to the gym I am bound. Why? What is the draw, the attraction, the force that persuades or, rather, compels me to attend the movement of heavy metal through a series of laborious sets and repetitions? A mystery.

I know what the motivations are for me, can only guess what they are for you, and suspect they in their variations coincide along the way. For this musclehead, the workouts have to be done, come rain or come shine. The value of yesterday's workout and other days gone by depends on today's; the workout of tomorrow and the days to follow are founded on the ones before them — in particular, the one upon which I am about to embark. No single training session is more important or less important than the other; they are equally important, fully important. They are intertwined, interwoven and interdependent, like words in the sentence of a complete and undefiled thought, a truth.

We say, "If I don't work out today, I'll work out tomorrow." But what do we say tomorrow if we don't work out tomorrow, "I'll work out next time."? And so the conversation goes until it fades to guilt or a forgotten subject.

I'm training this afternoon because it promises good — challenge, joy, exhilaration, reinforcement, order, stress relief, camaraderie and inner conversation — and links me securely and properly with the days ahead. I need to express myself physically that I might be healthy and whole. Daily activity and busy-ness fall short of this role and certainly do not provide sufficient exercise; they only accentuate the need for it.

This day is not just another day. What day in your life is "just another day"? Today is a miracle, one surprise after another, sometimes shouting, often whispering of the hope of more to come. The man or woman who thinks tritely of his or her life will endure a trite existence. This day, today, is the most important day.

Exactly your point, you say, why waste it or use it up in the gym under the iron? I say, so the sun will shine tomorrow, the next day and the next... in your heart, from your soul and upon your strong back.

As there are the moments, minutes and hours before the gym and its industry, there are the corresponding times after. Who among us is not disheveled and misshapen when we miss a scheduled workout? We outlive the discomfort, we rationalize our choice to forego exercise, we defend our lame excuses — after all, we are a free and unfettered people, not chained to the conventions of absolute discipline, or more appropriately, boring habit; we could use the rest and fun and, really, we do have forever — but our once-enthusiastic plans, the proper self-image we fashioned, the promises and commitments we made to ourselves to develop ourselves are weakened.

Where we might dread the resistance, the weights present and anticipate with shortness of breath a run on the endless, timeless treadmill and long for a stretch on the couch with the remote at our command, we are able to re-program our minds with thoughts of purpose and fulfillment, development and accomplishment. Don't weaken under the weight of the flesh and bones that beg for your attention. You're not lazy, lost or lifeless; it'll take more than a few poor choices and rationalizations to bury yourself in that infertile ground.

You're building a palace for tomorrow, rooms for the future, and the work is evident in the rising structure. The sketches are in your imaginative mind and alter with time and living day to day. The foundation is sound and development is taking place regularly beneath floorboards, casings and walls. Wiring and pipes and reinforcements and safety systems cannot be seen, yet your mighty hands install them.

It might require effort of mind and will, but think of the good of the pushing and pulling, filling the lungs with oxygen and the muscles with blood; the sensation of warm energy spreading through the body and the moisture of resolute toil worn like a cloak.

Oh, the thrill of a workout completed or the unbearable woe of yet another pushed aside. Gravity lifts me up, higher 'n' higher.

The sensations and convictions that drew me to the gym materialized in a series of slow-moving challenges between a barbell evidently bolted to the gym floor and me. I hadn't noted that the gravity in the vicinity of the lifting platform registered in the red zone late that Saturday afternoon. I loaded on the plates and proceeded to execute deadlifts (as I recall, it was the other way around; they executed me), six sets times 12, 10, 8, 6, 4, 2. I started with the bar and a plate and a half, or 185, for 12 reps. With each successive set, I added fifty pounds till the last set of 405 for two.

I don't know what's more hysterical, the high reps or the heavy weight.

Sufficiently warmed up, I continued my cheerful routine with four sets of 8 to 10 reps of widegrip bentover barbell rows supersetted with mid-weight, stiffarm pullovers using my favorite thick bar.

My stance is narrow. I bend low and grab the bar three inches from the collars and pull it high to the upper pec. The pull focuses on muscle action — contraction and extension — depending less on thrust and the physics of momentum to move the weight. Great for upper back width, thickness and power, and contributes to the strength of the lower back, quads and hamstrings. A comprehensive move, the rows add to the body's overall muscle growth. Careful, not designed for tykes.

The pullovers tug on those lats while allowing you to lie down on a bench, oxygenize, stretch and stare at the ceiling between the tough sets.

Press on and don't look back. A friend threw my battered body over his shoulder as he retreated to the juice bar for a protein shake to ensure his muscles would grow to outrageous proportions during his long drive home — waste not, time or muscle-making efficiency.

On the way he dumped me off at the cable-crossover where I knocked off five sets of 12 reps of the popular pec-defining exercise, a nice tie-in to the muscle-action of the pullover. This burning yet non-consuming exercise was completed in swift, meticulous form to achieve maximum pump and efficacy. Zoom, zoom.

What's this? I stood upright and rolled my shoulders back and noticed there was something missing below the scapula and along the lower sweep of the lats. Using my built-in MPS (Muscle Positioning System), I determined five supersets of one-arm rows blended with rounded-back dips would harmonize the un-sung regions and complete my composition for the day.

The bis and tris and thighs didn't go home this hungry Saturday without drawing blood, either. The whole greedy lot got in on the act. Did I mention I started with crunches and hanging leg raises? Yesiree.

Now maybe you'll recall the secret appeal that makes life without the weights regrettable. How quickly we forget.

Better check your fuel, ammo, parachute, helmet, socks and underwear.

There are days when a stimulating workout is sufficient and there are days when blasting it is essential. This awareness enables you to enter the gym without trepidation, overwhelming preconceptions or unrealistic expectations, which lead to disappointment. I enter the gym with the hope of doing the best I can and enjoying myself, embracing the work and enduring the pain. No one said it would be easy and no one said it must be monumental. Good workouts unfold like robust blooms on a thorn bush. Water them well, prune them and provide ample sunshine and shade.

Just Another Year

The countdown has begun. I must admit the recent years have come and gone like water dripping from a leaky faucet — a bit of a nuisance. Alas, I'm no plumber, can't stop the leak, and it continues wearing away the surface upon which it falls and gathering in pools around me. Though I'm clever and have managed to stay dry by seeking high ground, I look down and wonder how long it will be before my feet are wet, and the all-of-me? Don't tell me it's time for galoshes.

Who are we, where are we and what have we done; where are we going? As if it wasn't enough to have survived the past 365 days, we now have to answer a bunch of dumb personal questions.

It's not uncommon to review each year gone by, a convenient capsule of time, and assess our steps forward and steps back, and determine the place we presently abide. Either by tradition or perchance we count our blessings and total our troubles, score the wins and scorn the losses, value our wise moves and rationalize the foolish ones. Are we more or less, we wonder, better off or worse, bigger and stronger, fatter or leaner, and how is our health; how are our relationships, friendships and surroundings, our economics, finances and holdings, our standards, values and morals and how about our accomplishments this year and our possibilities for next?

At this juncture, if you're a drinking man or woman, you'll either put the bottle back on the shelf or pour yourself a tall one.

Wow! Aren't you glad you exercise hard, eat the right food and continually look forward? Those fine deeds and exemplary habits enable us to do good, endure the bad and resist the ugly that surrounds us. You and I admit that the world, except for the jerks, is a beautiful place and would be frightening and unbearable if we didn't lift weights and live wisely.

The weights fortify: They add strength to our shoulders, arms, back and legs to fight the enemy, and improve our physical health to resist disease and fatigue. Our character is broadened by their calling and they strengthen our spirit by humbling it. Get ye behind me, wiseguys.

They simplify: The order that comes from lifting weights provides order to the mind, ease to one's manners, and calm to the soul. Complexities are defused, snags are untangled and obstacles are overcome when the mind, body and soul are synchronized. One more rep and another... every rep counts... push that iron, Bomber.

They modify: Stress can kill and stress can sustain life. The weights, and lifting them with keenness, take stress by the

162

ear and bring it to practical submission. Resistance training and exercise use stress like a racecar utilizes a tank full of high-octane fuel — to win. How it got there isn't important, how it's dispersed is another story.

They amplify: The clang alone, as metal meets metal, is enough to arouse the emotions and spirits and adrenalin of a passionate lifter. A passionate lifter is anyone, male or female, young or old, who has lifted weights long enough to have gotten hooked for one reason or another, known or unknown. That would be you, me, us and any other bomber by any other name.

They magnify: Who can deny that lifting iron (and eating right — it's part of the package) doesn't clarify the objects and ojectives before you, make you see more clearly and more precisely and add to your creativity? Creativity, like understanding, is one's vision of life unveiled and highly magnified. Lift weights long enough — one tough workout will do it — and you see what you wouldn't if you hadn't. See what I mean? Sure you do.

They identify: You might know who you are, or think you know who you are, or want or need to know who you are. Good. That pile of iron and your will to lift it, those countless sets and innumerable reps, the distinct form and strict concentration — they are telling signs. Take note. Workout upon workout, day after day, consistently with intensity and resolve — they will give you a clue. Observe closely. Who you are is who you're becoming with the steel in your hands and the mettle in your heart. Lookin' good... who you are, that is.

They exemplify: There was a time when lifting weights was the weird choice of weird characters. Well, thank God, things have not changed too much. We're still at it and properly proud of it. No one is perfect, including lifters, whatever that means; some lead, some follow, some imitate. The act and the outcome — the work and the product — of weightlifters

163

and weight lifting vary with the generation and school from which they come.

Bombers do it because they love it (even when they don't), and something vitally important is missing when the weights are silent and still. They glow like a black star and thump like a single heartbeat; they soothe like an ointment, comfort like an old friend, satisfy like cool, clear water to the thirsty and give life like oxygen. They make us rich, yet very few grasp the solid advocate by the handle to shake it.

I wonder, if the weights made us money — hard, cold cash — would the tale to tell be different?

Do I hear someone saying, "Hey, Draper, ya go to the gym, do some benches with the guys, get a pump, go home and have a few beers. What's the big deal?" First of all, Bub, make that a protein shake.

Yup. He's the same guy who doesn't now how to fly an imaginary warship above the radar and bomb it. Go figure.

About this past year's workouts: I estimate of some 210 workouts, ten were disappointing (painful, unfulfilling, unsubstantial but acceptable — what should I do, throw them out?), fifty were merely sufficient — they did the job, a hundred were quite satisfactory (orderly, focused, well paced and gratifying) and fifty were superior (sets, reps or weight in excess of expectation, pump and form superior, well-being and rewards exceptional). Not bad for a kid.

About my next workout: It will be no recordsetter, but, according to the year's previous records, it will be thrilling. I shall not demand too much of myself, which is a sure way to achieve plenty. I shall work the gut out of fear and obligation, and go on to things left undone (anything that doesn't hurt) with whatever mood accompanies me on the gym floor. This could mean lighter weight and quicker pace with a grin, or a focused stare of contentment to match a slower pace and a battle against the pleasant gravity of the iron.

I plan to make no enemies of the metal, racks, cables and benches. We are partners this day, and have many more interlockings before us. Civility — nay, more than that — kinship is to be sought from this day forth. I'm aggrieved by unneeded enemies and unwanted foe. I'll fight the good fight, but I'll seek no danger. Lengthen the years of my physical banter and play is my quest, not body-breaking battles to see who's the best.

Blast to last and be the last to blast.

That's what I always say.

What do we do? Where do we start? The first thing to do is consider the truth of what has been declared about fat, lazy and irresponsible, and the consequences of the overweight condition: diabetes, heart attack, stroke, cancers, hypertension; and the daily symptoms and side effects: weakness, immobility, low energy, low self-esteem, apathy; and the woeful world realities: medical costs, insurance rates, job availability, the shortened lifespan.

Obesity is personal terrorism. Where does it end?

We know what to do. Exercise, eat right, now and for good.

Most overweight problems end when we decide to end them.

Monday, Monday.
Two More Reasons to Lift Weights

It's Monday morning and you look at the alarm clock like it was time bomb. You're not a violent person, but you want to snatch the cunning device and toss it out the window before it explodes in your face. You calm your displeasure, drag your sorry butt out of bed and direct it toward the bathroom door. Mondays are like that.

Dead man walking.

You're about to face the world of struggling masses who regard the first day of the week as you do, anxiously, fearfully, irritably and regrettably. Hmmph! No relief from that sorry mob. "Why was I born?" you ask, as the toilet flushes and you mount the merciless scale behind the door. Was it bad luck, an accident, poor planning, spite, a quirk of fate, a sick joke? Cloudy thoughts not worth registering pass through your mind while your eyes focus on the tell-tale dial vacillating between your bare feet.

You strain to see the numbers and wonder why. No one wins at this juncture of life. If you've gained weight, you're fat; if you've lost weight, you're skinny; if your weight remains the same, nothing's happened in spite of all your hard work. You knew it all along. Why bother? Mondays are cruel.

The kitchen is more hopeful. By now the teeth are brushed and the face is washed and a coffee pot sits on the countertop like a genie. At the flick of a switch it growls and snarls like a well-trained leopard and the aroma of Columbia's finest rises from its steaming crown. Yeah, life's a struggle, you muse with sudden inexplicable generosity, and how frivolous it would be if it was predictable and trouble-free. Where's my mug?

One cube of sugar isn't gonna kill ya any more than one cup of coffee — so what if the cup's the size of a mixing bowl. And, yes, that bran muffin looks like cake, but it really is a bran muffin, full of useful carbs and whole grains and fiber. The protein from which big muscles are made comes from the super shake made with 16 ounces of low-fat milk, a small banana, a cup of protein powder, a half-cup of papaya juice and ice. Mmm, enough for two servings. You're rich. Kitchens have been known to transform despair into hopefulness and build strong bodies twelve ways.

Kitchens also prepare you to leave your fortress and confront the throng. First stop, the gym. Only the strong survive and you're not taking any chances. It's barely dawn, a pathetic sacrifice, but worth the pain. Start the day by moving a ton of steel and the rest seems like a walk in the park. It's also comforting to know you're not the only crazy person on the planet.

They're a good bunch, the 6 AM crowd. But then, who's gonna start trouble this hour of the morning? You nod and smile (small lies) while you stumble around the gym floor; everything's a haze. The stationary bike looks like a wild thing as you mount it from the side. Whoa, boy... easy. After some brutal prodding and coaxing, the legs begin pumping and the miles roll on by. You're warming up and letting go and the internal juices are kicking in. The world is a nice place when the heart and lungs are in sync and the endorphins are released in abundance. Your black and white world fills with color, and a real smile worth a fortune covers your face. With two fingers to the carotid artery, you note you're coming to life at last.

What day is it? It's Monday. How could you forget? But that's not what you mean. You're over the Monday thing. It's chest-and-back day. That is, of course, after gut 'cuz a weekend can do weird things to the abdominal area. Besides, you're not quite ready for presses and deadlifts yet.

You notice most lifters train midsection in a half-hearted manner. You don't see them performing their array of ab exercises with the same intent and intensity as bench presses and standing curls. They crunch without any functional extension or tight, purposeful contraction. When performing leg raises, they flounder about without muscular focus or control — fish out of water. They roll about on big rubber balls or do twists with bars across their backs until something gets tired or they give up. What's that?

Tough section, the midsection. It manages to collect fat efficiently and hide muscle successfully without any help at all. Knocking out sets and reps without witnessing a gleaming six-pak — most everyone's secret dream — can be a nightmare. And the exercises available for developing a lean muscular waist are about as much fun and effective as paddling... upstream... in a leaky boat. We're sinking fast, Captain.

Keep paddling. Paddle harder.

So much for the gut and onto the real stuff, chest and back. Whoever invented the bench press must be worth a small fortune. Probably has shoulder injuries, as well. The royalties alone could make him a multimillionaire. Everyone knows the exercise; tell a little girl in pre-school that you lift weights and she'll immediately ask, "How much can you bench press?" She can't ride a bike and she wants to know your bench.

The bench press is popular even though it's not all that good for musclebuilding, causes injuries and it's commonly done wrong. Go to any gym and watch the eager trainees. They lift their butt off the bench while arching their back till the bar touches their ribcage (one rep); they bounce the bar off their chest like it was a truck spring (two reps); the right side goes up long before the left side (three reps); the bar comes halfway down and goes almost all the way up (four reps); the bar comes down on the body hard and stays down while the lifter gasps and squeals and gets assistance from a nearby innocent victim… he strains his back for life (five reps); and finally the plates on the left side slide off the bar followed immediately by the plates on the right side — end of lift. High fives all around! What a champ!

I say use dumbbells whenever you have a choice.

The bar in all its rigidness prevents you from rotating the hands just enough to engage the pecs correctly and fully. Dumbbells offer this advantage. Further, the unyielding hand position forces the deltoid's joint-like mechanics to remain fixed throughout the entire exercise. This control causes unnatural shoulder tracking and a subsequent impingement of tissue and nerve. Injury eventually rears its ugly head as power and intensity are applied. Does this ring a bell, bombers? Another seldom-considered benefit of dumbbell training is the powerful clean necessary to set the weights in place, and the fight to return them to the starting position and back in the rack upon

exercise completion. This is called good old-fashioned work —
bull work — that builds the body in functional and muscle-
energy connected ways that racked barbell exercises do not
and cannot. Go for it.

Guys, you crave cantaloupe delts? Duh! Dumbbell inclines
at 45 to 75 degrees do the job like no other exercise. Girls, you
want strong, lovely and substantial shoulders that ripple when
you smile? Wow! Dumbbell inclines. They tie the shoulder
into the upper- and mid-pectorals, exalting the upper body.
Triceps are fired up and the serratus scream to be heard. Biceps
and forearms fight gallantly to get the iron in position, keep it
there throughout the set and return it to its starting place. You
always wanted to move the iron… now you're movin' the iron.
And your back with all its powerful parts isn't exactly hangin'
out lookin' for odd jobs and minimum wage. It's working overtime, pulling, pushing and pressing.

Dumbbell presses in their variety of angles and grooves
work both front and side shoulders as well as the whole pectoral range. I'm not shooting the bench press in the foot; I'm
suggesting you use it smartly, enjoy it and don't put a crown on
it. A baseball cap placed backwards will do. While you're at it,
add cable crossovers to your chest routine and bentover lateral
raises that somewhat resemble rows — go heavier than usual
with a sufficient thrust to build some needed mass back there.
Bentover tweakies don't do the job. Tweakies don't work anywhere, anytime. Tweakies are for tweaks.

Being a responsible professional and an anti-tweaker, I
would be remise if I didn't emphasize the need for heavy back
work for thickness and density, as well as profuse lat work for
width and dramatic taper. According to moods, urges and needs,
I alternate between bentover barbell rows, dumbbell rows and
seated lat rows for power and mass. I often throw in widegrip
pulldowns to the front as a secondary set to chest and

shoulder pressing (supersetting). I enjoy pulldowns behind the neck as well, as they mimic the famous overhead double-biceps pose hit under heavy lighting by bodybuilding champions. Very inspirational, most effective.

Close-grip pulldowns work well as an moody change of pace. The under-grip pulldown tears lovingly at the lats, serratus and biceps, a very cool movement when hoping, wishing and dreaming of hitting biceps on an off-arm day. Toss in some stiffarm pullovers for sets of 8 to 12 for further lat stimulation, a tug on the tris and an exhilaration nearing euphoria.

Look at the clock, the day's half over. We never want to chase time away, bombers. That's why we lift weights: to spirit us through yet another Monday, to make the best of the hours we have, to learn to appreciate our presence on the earth and, I dare say, to extend the number of our days of maximum fulfillment. Besides, we want to be strong and have big muscles.

If your plane doesn't fly, push it.

Confusion Brings Clarity Where None Exists

Life happens in spite of our brilliant efforts. In fact, it is quite independent of our presence, continuing miraculously with or without our input. Not only is the incredible force apart from our management, it is creative and unpredictable.

We know a few things. Some days are better than others. Ah, yes! Some days are worse. Oh, no! Amateur examination tells us we cannot ordinarily attribute the superiority or inferiority of any single day to any single thing. Several matters — conditions, happenings — account for noticeable daily differences. Life, and our existence, we conclude, is simply complicated.

More than complicated, life's a mystery. Everything can be going superbly well — the weather, eating, rest, attitude, relationships, work, bank balance, stress levels, hair — yet your time in the gym becomes a minor catastrophe. You enter the asylum of clanging iron and gravity gushes into your body through every pore, scratch, pinprick and orifice. At first this phenomenon is unapparent; everything looks and smells the same.

"Hi, guys... doll," the latter salutation accompanied by an imperceptible wink. Ladies love that stuff. Your voice is deep, words articulate. The only gal in the room is bigger than you and threatens to report you to the authorities for sexual harasment. Me and my big mouth.

You retreat, drop your gym bag in its private space, retrieve a water bottle and needed gear and choose the starting point for the big attack; dumbbell inclines are in your sights. The tris flex, the lats are thrown into place with sufficient effort. "Stand back, muscle mutts, the sparks are gonna' fly. Yes siree, Bob." This you mutter under your breath, as you walk a circle around Brunhilda, who's glaring.

No siree, ma'am. Not today, Annie Mae. Ain't so, Billy Jo. The weights you tug for a warm-up feel like they're painted to the rack... good thing no one was looking, big guy. What's that all about? Your tail curls between your legs and you scamper to the corner like a scolded monkey, where you sit quietly nursing your water bottle. The iron has a way of keeping us humble.

"A lesson in life. I should be grateful." The noble thought crosses your mind, while considering your next move, but wisdom and magnanimity are not your strengths. You're stricken, stunned and devastated. Those dumbbells, the nasty immovable ones stuck permanently to the rack, are girly dumbbells. More water, scowling and despair.

There's a season and reason for all things, jet jockeys. It's time to grow up, if you can't grow strong. You concede, but you do not surrender. Unable to move the iron, you fake a decent midsection workout. A mild performance of crunches, leg raises and rope tucks is stimulating and gives you space to hide out, recover emotionally and prepare a new approach.

Within fifteen minutes of counting sets and reps, rhythmically extending and contracting and pacing, you feel warm and invigorated, invested and reassured. Monkey-man has left the body and gorilla-boy is assuming his place. Perhaps small gorilla can sneak up on small weights for a small workout. Humility tastes like rust to the palate, but is titanium to the soul.

There are times when we must put our expectations in our back pockets and save them for another day. The body in all its understanding speaks to us loud and clear. We must learn to listen, and speak its language. This is tricky, requiring willingness and close attention for a long, long time.

You're feeling mildly philosophical. Defeat does that to the driven, a strategy of survival to conceal one's personal weakness. It doesn't take a doc to tell us we have our ups and downs. One day you've got it, next day you don't. Life is peaks and valleys. You win a few and lose a few. It all evens out in the end. You take the good with the bad. Go with the flow. One day you're up, the next day you're down. Don't sweat it. You can't win 'em all. Here today, gone tomorrow. That's life!

Your originality, clear thinking, acute perception and understanding spirit are inspiring. You move on without impediment like freshly erupted lava on the slopes of time. You're hot.

A willing spirit and immovable weights, an odd couple make. A quick review of possible relevant influences should explain the negative training response. Hair, like the tightness of one's t-shirt, is not the least of the factors prominently affecting one's successful workout. Still, I'd be checking bodyweight, muscle fatigue from previous training sessions, regularity of water consumption and protein intake, insufficient muscle recovery due to improper rest or inadequate nutrients, or false or misread well-being indicators.

You're experiencing a slump. It's decided. A slump is like the silence between musical beats. There's no rhythm in blues, no rock in rock 'n' roll and no mo in Mozart without the silence between the beats. Slumps are good, necessary and unavoidable; you gotta learn to use 'em. Using slumps means greeting them knowingly and enduring them with courage, hope and confidence. Thank God for slumps and the teaching they provide.

There are other conflicting combos, more common, that throw you for a loop. Recognizing them is part of the solution. Been there, seen this?

You feel tough as steel, yet you can't face the iron's noisy, cold and stubborn sameness — not today. You'd rather be bowling and you hate bowling. Almost literally you feel tentacle-like grips clutching and tugging you away from the gym. You wriggle and writhe... toward the gym, in the exit, out the entrance. You squirm and struggle. You're ready to submit. Don't you dare, not even! Whatta ya think this is, pre-school and lollipops? You think you can go home 'cuz you don't wanna play muscles today?

Stand strong. Push that iron. Lift that steel. Count those reps... and do two more. Stay home today and tomorrow never comes... just another day. You call it freedom to do as you please. Call it weak and submissive, spineless and snivelling. A dumbbell is a dumbbell is a dumbbell.

And then there are the times you crawl to the gym in a cold sweat, temperatures in triple digits and you've got the shakes. "No power on earth can keep me from my workout, man... cough, cough... I just gotta get my hands on the iron.

It's, like, my best friend… gag, snort, sniffle." Train today and everybody in the gym gets sick and you die tomorrow at dawn. Don't run your body down, man. Go home, feed it chicken soup, stay warm and — special concession — watch the tube without guilt. You can't hustle nature. She's lovable, but she's stubborn.

Wait a minute. I almost forgot about the ironheaded, steel-brained, mono-minded bodybuilder, as if that were at all possible. A large number of bodybuilders are authentic, card-carrying fanatics, which offend healthy, well-balanced musclebuilders and drives their non-bodybuilding friends nuts. Is that all you think about: lifting weights, eating protein, training like animal, getting huge, getting ripped, milk cartons, egg whites, protein shakes, bench presses, deadlifts, squats and your one-rep max? Get a life, Gorgeous. You ain't gonna be Governor or marry the prettiest and brightest girl on the farm if all you can do is stack plates, count reps and beat eggs. Get a job, read something besides *Flex*, watch something besides *Pumping Iron*, have a pizza, resist shaving your body for a week, and, no, I will not put oil on your back. We don't want to see your latest posing routine adapted to Ravel's Bolero in D minor.

You're going to overtrain, burn out, short circuit your central nervous system, go into catabolism and implode. You'll wake up one day and refuse to go to the gym ever again the rest of your life. Iron will become your enemy. You'll grow hairy and get fat. What then? They'll kick sand in your face. Lighten up.

How about the guy and gal who never miss a workout, yet never quite work out? They arrive on time and leave on time, but nothing worth remembering happens in between. They stretch, roll around on a floor mat, mount the stationary bike, do some curls and presses with a pair of nifty chrome weights, sip from their official ESPN water bottles and unfold and refold their authentic Nike sweat towela. At the first sign of perspiration, however, they slow down, cool off and shower. Pain and strain along with gain go mainly down the drain.

Health is wealth and organic vegetables keep them slim and regular. "We have boundless energy," they say. Ha! They wouldn't recognize the stuff if they tripped over it.

There are basic rules we discover when common sense is allowed to accompany us along life's merry flight. Keep 'er steady as she goes, bombers. Use the tailwinds, butt the headwinds and never let 'er stall. Depend on steady cruising for most of your journey; soar when you're inspired and glide when you must. Autopilot is for airheads — you want to get where you're going and be there along the way. If you're prone to air sickness, stay focused; closely attend your mighty pursuit, appreciate its fascinating actions, welcome the benefits and anticipate the rewards. How many people do you know who can fly? There are so few of us with wings.

Here's a plan for the sufficiently initiated, slightly committed, yet very willing man or woman, guy or gal, lady or gentleman, teen or kid... with guts.

Walk 'n' jog a mile and do fifty crunches and fifty leg raises, three alternate days a week. On the remaining three or four days go to the gym and do four basic exercises that complement each other, three or four sets of 8 to 10 repetitions of each exercise. Pretend a secret admirer is watching you and you want to impress him or her with your strength of body and mind. In other words, do your best.

Eat and sleep smartly. Eat more protein, less sugar and eat more regularly. Sleep like a child, innocent and carefree. Train like an animal of choice each workout: rabbit, grizzly bear, lion, swamp turtle, moose, spotted gazelle, short-haired anteater or Secaucus swine.

Too simple? Good. That's the way it should be. We think complex is better, but it ain't. You want to fortify the mix, add home-grown confidence, regularity and plain hard work — a concoction more powerful than jet fuel.

As I was exiting the gym after a battle with the steel — in which I considered myself the victor, though I was battered and dragging — it occurred to me that defeat was not a condition I experienced through the rugged years of metal wars. There were the times when dumbbells or plates were released mistakenly and landed on my feet, or those grim occasions when I was ailing and, by a two-hour workout, over-extended my body's resistance to exorcise the bug, but these were important lessons and needed to be learned. Victories in disguise.

And, you can be sure, defeat has a way of disguising victory, like lifting and never straining, even slightly, and doing the same three safe exercises each time you attend the gym once or twice a week for thirty minutes, twenty of which are spent stretching and warming up, meditating and yoga, reading and exchanging views on the weather. There are more, of course, like...

Not blasting it when you can and should

Passing on your ab work 'cuz it's boring

Not squatting or deadlifting 'cuz they're hard

Working arms again 'cuz you can't think of anything else and you want big arms bad

Doing the first six easy reps of a set and not the last two hard reps that count

Skipping legs entirely 'cuz you walk a lot and think that's enough

Daydreaming the moment the serious lifting has begun

Looking for relief or fulfillment anywhere other than the muscle under load — a little pump, a little burn, a little conversation with the cute thing in the corner.

Much to Say About Nothing

Morning, and I was slouched at my desk poking at an open can of sardine filets with my fork. Been a long time since these little guys splashed around in the ocean, I thought. I gave myself a "D" for posture, sat up and arched my back into a tight contraction. Feels good to straighten, stretch and contract. Sardines are good for you, did you know that? Omega-3 oil, high in protein, no carbs, smelly and not too appetizing. I like the crunchy little bones. Oops! Slouching again — another "D". What time is it, anyway?

Time for another cup of coffee. I wonder if coffee and sardines are a bad mix. I know they're not a good mix, like tuna and water, but, are they bad? You know, like, do they produce enzyme malfunctions or corrupt hormonal activity when they're combined? Is the protein neutralized by the caffeine or do the Omega-3s turn rancid and become triglycerides? Coffee and Danish pastry go well together. I love Danish pastry. I haven't had a piece of Danish since I was a kid living at home... 16, maybe. I wonder if it tastes the same. Huh, 45 years and no Danish.

Still raining. Going on three weeks. It's been raining for so long that I'm getting into it. The world gets small. The darkness and the haze limit the distance you can see and the blue sky is gone, cloaked in grey and brooding clouds. You go out only when you must, to run errands, go to work, the gym, church... wherever... and you mostly look down, or from the underside of an umbrella if you're with your wife or girlfriend. Guys don't use umbrellas, unless they're business guys, which I am not. No wingtips and knee-high socks, though I do have a couple of ties and a jacket somewhere.

The indoors is where it's at. The crackling, flickering hearth is the center of attraction as I feed the fire according to its appetite. It's warm, comfortable, alluring, hopeful and alive. Homemade soups and stews nourish the body, heal the wounds and soothe the spirit. Shelter takes on new meaning and you're grateful to be living, breathing, working and protected.

The gym, always a refuge, becomes a special place away from your digs. It's good to mingle, hear your voice among other voices and bear the struggle of unkind and peculiar weather with like creatures — friends, indeed. Between sets I go to the gym's open back door to peer at the rain and inhale the fresh wet air. Very nice. I don't gaze too long 'cuz I don't want to lose my rhythm or body warmth or pump or concentration or favorite bench. The rain's nice, but not that nice.

Fewer people make it to the gym when the wet weather moves in. Traffic slows down, wet clothing, hair and feet are uncomfortable, and, like I said, the world becomes small. And inconvenient. The gym seems far away: into a hooded slicker, out the front door, beyond the gloom, through the downpour, puddles and mud and across the flooded intersections. Cars are slipping and sliding, and who can see through the windshield in weather like this? It's confusing and messy. Wipers and heaters and defrosters work overtime. The carwash is empty. So are the swings, barbeque pits, street corners, park benches and jogging paths. A little lonely — you can feel it. Just you and yourself.

Ah! A good group: serious, dedicated, appreciative; industrious, willing and able. They're getting their money's worth, investing in their health, wasting no time and increasing their personal wealth. They're working out. This is entertainment at its best — beneficial, exclusive and confidential. Nothing like a little active privacy and treasure hunting on a rainy day, that's what I always say. It may or may not cross their minds, but somewhere in their consciousness they know they are where they belong, safe and sound and dry and pumped, and it's teeming outside. The black afternoon sky is emptying itself and they're doing chins and bentover rows. Ha. I mean, the power could go out, lightning could strike or the forceful wind could blow off the roof, yet here we are, the intrepid few. I'd hang onto a 50-pound dumbbell if I were you.

I'm into my workout. How much I lift isn't as important as the very fact that I'm lifting in the powerful and secure confines of the darn-near-sacred gym. I move the iron with a different effort that arises from a palette of multiple strengths, desires and needs. Desire is the predominant factor affecting the shape and outcome of the action before me.

The music and clang and shuffling bodies don't compete with the hush that prevails. The symptoms of the weather have become almost endearing and penetrate the edges of our minds and souls. We need the rain, the water that gives life. I hate droughts. You won't see me moving to the moon anytime soon. Moon Gym will have to wait. Later, Mars Health Club and Spa. World Gym is for the stars.

I find a corner of the gym and practice sidearm lateral raises. This once-favorite shoulder movement had been relegated to the exercise junkyard after a dumb accident disconnected my right infraspinatus, an important rotator cuff support mechanism. Since that fateful day twenty-five years ago, the shoulders, the poor mutts, have had to eat scraps and work hard for their run on the beach. Today, prompted by a calm thoughtfulness and nostalgia resulting from the confinement of inclement weather, I decide to revisit the long-lost friend. I'm in the mood for discovery, or re-discovery, as the case may be.

Just to assume the starting position — slightly crouched with the dumbbells held fixed and ready before me — and exert the outward and upward action with that particular shoulder contraction at the peak would be enough, no matter how light the resistance. I start with five pounds and exact the movement. Twenty-five years later and I feel a chill of rebirth. I know that groove, like an old song when I was happy and growing up with my buds. How does it go again? I go to the 10s, brace my body and retrace the groove. At ten reps I'm burning and pumping and singing in the rain. Draper's smiling.

I grab the 15-pounders like they were my third and final attempt at setting a new world record: tense, deliberate, prepared for the high risk, yet confident with hope and faith and need. I can do it. With extraordinary focus, rep upon rep I fight my way to another stunning 10 reps. The muscle activity is real, the pump and burn are not imaginary and I devour the encouragement.

The telltale twang on the last reps didn't scare me, but gave me kind warning. Be smart, bomber known for making crash landings in dangerous territory. Go slowly. Build up and support the area surrounding the absent spinatus muscle to permit further action, heavier weight, tighter contraction, greater overload and enable the delts to assume the proportions and consistency of watermelons... um... make that cantaloupes. Grapefruits? Two more sets with the 15s and we'll sneak up on the reluctant exercise over the next months. I'll need to fashion a new groove.

I'm singing and dancing in the rain.

There are four of us standing at the back door, none of us fighting to get out first. The rain is inviting, but wet nonetheless. We agree the miserable weather conditions are good for the dry landscape and our spoiled-rotten nature. We're done here today, thank God, and better prepared for tomorrow. Not one is taller than the other, race and gender don't matter and any one of us would carry the other if he or she asked. We're in this together.

See ya later... Friday... next week for me... stay dry... don't slip on the stairs. Hey, the days are getting longer, ya know... yeah, right, it doesn't get dark till 5:00 now... less than three months to spring... spring, what's that?

I hop in my faithful truck, crank it over, throw it in gear and it's off to the castle, James, and don't spare the horses. Or should I say, raise the spinnaker, mates, and head due south.

In truth, bombers take to the sky despite the season, weather conditions, moods or moon risings.

If during your workouts you find yourself daydreaming regularly, review your training commitment. The imagination is a wonderful thing; enjoy it and may it serve you well. But don't allow the creative wandering to replace focus where focus is essential. A workout without focus is half a workout, and the least effective half at that. A workout interspersed with daydreaming is akin to playing. One is going through the motions when one is exercising and thinking of something other than the exercise. There are few things more liberating and profound and exhilarating and constructive and fascinating than total concentration. The only way to grow strong, muscular and healthy is through focused and wise training and eating.

Daydream on that awhile.

Attitude Awareness, Adjustment and Finesse

Forgive me, please. I'm given to generalizations, forgetting there's a world beyond my own. Self-centered, I guess you'd call it, the regrettable condition to which we all as individuals frequently succumb. Of course, we prefer kinder terms to describe our egoism — point of view, perspective, opinion and attitude do nicely. Whatever, attitudes, like old-fashioned single-band radios, require constant tuning to eliminate the static and communicate the sound, the message loud and clear.

Babies have been born, couples have married, somebody's won, another has lost and someone's got a new puppy. Things will never be the same. Their world has changed forevermore. Enter the emergency room or ICU of any hospital, the red zone in Iraq or a stricken beach fronting the Indian Ocean, in each place another episode unfolds, another scene is witnessed, another view observed and story told.

Some points of view, perspectives and attitudes are fixed by circumstances. Some circumstances are fixed by points of view, perspectives and attitudes. Knowing this, if we care, the smart thing to do is accentuate the latter and decentuate the former. We ought to take control of our circumstances, bombers, wherever and whenever we can. Think right, act right — an artful and effortful cooperation.

For this mad bodybuilder, working shoulders and chest is like vigorously grasping and passionately fondling hot coals in the hope of achieving a mean burn in the delts and a sizzling pump in the pecs. I wrap the right wrist and elbow, employ my improvised thick-grip device, use hand pads and push with all my might. Volcanoes do not erupt, but smoke billows from their craters.

The bar of the Smith Press goes up slowly. (I hear snickering.) The facial expressions that accompany the stunted exercise are hideous. I add weight with each set, striving for maximum muscle contraction in the deltoids. One does what one must do. What I achieve is magnified pain and amplified facial distortions, including bulging eyes, quivering lips and an extended, thrashing tongue. By now I'm gurgling. Witnesses unaccustomed to my display of horrors try not to look, but they're transfixed. They wonder, is this an act? Is he having a seizure, will he explode, should I break out my cell and dial 911, is this what happens to aging champs too proud to let go?

I complete the last rep of the unsightly set with aplomb, promptly rise and confidently stride to the cable machine for widegrip pulldowns behind the neck. "Oh, no. He's going for the kill!" These I do with a blissful smile and subdued whimpers of contentment. "He's crazy," they correctly conclude and go back to their own business. They're new; they haven't seen anything yet.

Right about now is the perfect time for attitude awareness or more specifically, attitude adjustment and development. Construction of bis and tris and thighs will surely follow. There's absolutely no doubt in my mind that how we think affects who we are and how we perform. Approach life with enthusiasm and high hopes and we aspire; fulfilled and encouraged we look forward to tomorrow. View the day before us with gloom and defeat and by the day's end we are another step back and suffering. Tomorrow things will surely get worse. Woe is me.

Here we note two distant viewpoints with most of us falling somewhere in between.

Attitudes are tricky and require our attention and support, practice and tender-loving care. They just happen if we let them, which is fine when they're good. But a good attitude is not a sure thing in a world full of snakes, snarling beasts, tsunamis, hurricanes, floods, RPGs and IEDs. We need to develop them like our muscles and cardiovascular systems. Attitudes need help and hard work.

I don't mean pumping up our attitudes with air — foul air, at that — by sucking in the contemporary cliches and hoaxes stuck in our face by commercial TV and universal teaching: you can be and do anything you want, live your dreams, take control of your life, think big-live big, you are who you think you are. Nope. This huffing and puffing is as valid and worthwhile as a doctorate from smartypantsdegrees.com. This stuff does more to dull our minds and sharpen our desires to buy something we don't need: more beer, exotic perfume, brighter hair coloring or a Caddy SUV.

Get real.

How to Build Confidence, Wealth, Relationships or Sales in Ten Days and other books and tapes on winning can assist us in outlining some mental techniques and point us in a definite direction, but is it the right direction, or toward greed, power and self-centeredness? The devil's adornments we do not need and dare not embrace. Keep your eyes and ears open, eager readers of how-to hot tips, and glean the gems from the jelly beans.

Consider this, bombardiers: Attitude, our so-called state-of-mind as we enter upon our daily activities, is not so much an intellectual position as it is a condition of the heart. We don't proceed with our training and say it will be this way or that, and therefore succeed or fail. In real terms we win or lose because of our abilities, inherent and developed, and the heart and soul that accompany them. Of course, the mind is not disconnected, but at some point the less we rely on it the better we perform. The heart and soul in their union look and smell like one's instincts and truths, powerful allies. These noble advocates, when active in a man or woman, prompt excitement and certainty and action, a potent concoction.

Attitude, because of its essential role and influence in our lives, must be regularly attended. This is done not with a tool, a mantra or the rod, but with vigilance, loving persuasion and downright suffering need. Attitude must be sought, deveoped, honored and nurtured. Pessimism and thoughts of defeat must be treated as yapping dogs whose bite will never reach our ankles. Chase them away with a snarl from the gut; they cower when we show them our contempt.

I offer my deep insights, as usual, after much wonder, empirical research, sound guesswork, tea-leaf readings and the liberal use of my trusty Thesaurus. No sense going forward with the surrounding facts and enlightenments if we doubt their reliability, right? Right!

This has probably happened to you: You're heading for the gym in a rage because life is unfair; there are jerks everywhere, vehicles appear to be parked on the freeways, bills are piling up and time is slipping away. You forgot all about the significance of your workout, how it restores your balance and revitalizes the body and mind. Your attitude is revolting and, like lint on your favorite t-shirt, you've failed to notice and fix it. Small thing, big consequences. You arrive at the gym a mess.

The weights are ugly, heavy, dull and pointless. Not. You're head's screwed on wrong, Rude Dude, but don't despair. You notice the misalignment, the first requirement to a healthy mind, and it's never too late to make amends. Right attitude. Anyone else would have said, "What's the use? I'm miserable and I'm outta' here. See ya." Wrong attitude.

Bomber Principle Number One: A good attitude reaps a good workout and a good workout harvests a good attitude. Conversely, a crummy attitude reaps a crummy workout and so on.

Be aware of the power of habit, good and bad. Habits can make or break you, skydivers. They can be the wind beneath your wings, or the turbulence that cause you to crash.

Do not fall victim to the downward cycle; you're in control of this one. And don't merely put on a happy face. False does not work well around iron and steel, muscle and might. You need a real-life attitude adjustment, now. Here's where you must recall the worth of your positive perspective, the consequences of your negative perspective, the strength you gain and internally display and the good-time feeling you enjoy when you choose the former, and the utter dismay of the latter. I'd rather rot than suffer dismay, wouldn't you?

Bomber Principle Number Two: Attitude and its glory must be recognized, called forth, embraced and practiced regularly — or in a single word, cultivated.

You are cultivating, the farmer bomber at work in fields of metal. I'd rather be flying.

Maintain your attitude and your altitude, bomb squad. Fly high.

You know what we need, doesn't cost a darn thing — it's not cheap, but free? Daily encouragement, the simple well-wishing with unquestionable sincerity that comes in various forms when you least expect it — a smile, an appreciative nod, a strong handshake, a heartfelt pat on the back, a hug and a whisper of approval, an outspoken and spontaneous commendation before the whole gang. A person might be a breath from quitting, yet a meaningful expression from the corner of your mouth, "Push... you've got it," can inspire him to set a personal record.

"You're looking good, lost some size around the middle," truly conveyed, can save a person from canceling his or her gym membership, kicking the dog and binging on the pizza and beer all weekend.

Ah, but beware. Do not commend the person who in no way deserves it and, thereby, contribute to his conceit or drain his humility. We don't need another arrogant bodybuilder running loose.

The Contest: To Enter or Not to Enter

In our hemisphere we're entering the season of physique contests, summer and early fall, prime time to be in shape after the sunless winter hibernation and bulking, after the fair-weather spring revival and renewed muscular focus. Hundreds of shows are in production from the Mr. and Ms. Contra Costa to the famed Big Boy contest of Malibu, the Muscle Beach to the Olympia.

These are the times that try the souls of budding body-builders, the up and coming musclebuilders determined to give it a shot. The dais, the lights, the oil and pump, your favorite throbbing music — double-overhead biceps — one, two, three — down into a three-quarter back shot, slowly leaning, right arm raised skyward — flex, relax, flex. You and the crowd.

We're a competitive creature, if not with the person beside us, within ourselves. Unless a person is neurotic, this is good, causes us to strive to become better and better, perhaps the best. Competition is seductive, however, and can cause us to lose our balance. Be careful. Oh, yes, there's pride, that thin rivulet of vanity that trickles thru our being like the mighty Mississippi. Its power can not be estimated. No gauge has been devised by man to measure its limits.

I was in a Piggly Wiggly market in Georgia restocking an ice chest when I noticed a big guy following me around the fruits and vegetables. He finally cornered me by the frozen foods and asked how he could get ripped; he had a contest in six weeks. I stood there, looked at my wife and she looked at me. He went on to say he noticed I had veiny forearms, that he weighed 270 pounds at five-foot, ten-inches and got down to 240 pounds last year for the local show, but that didn't cut it. He shrugged his shoulders and in despair asked, "What should I do?"

In spite of the question and the fact that he didn't know who I was, he turned out to be intelligent and a nice guy. When you're 40 pounds overweight and six weeks from showtime, you tend to babble. He was with his wife, and half my age, training for ten years. A brute with thick traps — he could pull a freight train.

This is what I had to say.

If I were you, I'd reconsider entering the contest. You're too far out at this stage of the game. You have mass, shape, separation and tone, but you don't have the muscularity to impress the judges. You can diet down, but it'll cost you a fortune in muscle mass to lose the bodyfat. The next six weeks will be a nightmare as you watch yourself decrease in size and painfully notice your strength and energy diminish.

He was a black guy with soft eyes who had the word POWERLIFTER written over his chest, traps and shoulders. He nodded in unison with his wife as I spoke. "I hate to lose size," he muttered with reluctance yet conviction. His wife shook her head and rolled her eyes, declaring, "He's already complaining he's getting too small."

There are no secrets you don't already know, no ingredients this side of the pharmacist's counter. No supersetting, no bombing or blitzing system that'll do a healthy restructuring for you at this point in time. The most you can do is sacrifice this year's hard mass-gaining work by starving yourself and senselessly overtraining in the next forty-five days. Not smart.

Don't take drugs!

Do this instead. Get a pair of tickets and watch the show from the balcony. Use the bodyweight you have to continue your hard and heavy training. Stay tight in building muscle density and separation as you serve yourself an abundance of protein and carbs needed for repair, resistance and drive. Don't be gluttonous or menu-careless; be wise and generous. Be happy and enthusiastic.

Build your body core over the next year, establishing muscle maturity, training wisdom through creative experience and persistence. Don't toss your mighty delts and arms in quest of a biceps vein or a cut in the obliques.

We parted, wishing each other well. I don't know what he decided, but his wife was smiling.

I see the same phenomenon year after year when the spirit of competition rises in the gym. It's exciting, it's healthy, it's a solid goal. Know yourself and enter when you're ready for the experience and the fun of it. Drop a few pounds of the excess, increase the training pace and go in thumbs-up.

But, don't beat yourself up and waste time in search of an ab at the expense of your biceps when it's simply too soon.

Almost everyone you encounter today faces the overweight dilemma. They're either a little or a lot overweight and probably under-muscled and under-conditioned. The grand and outstanding difference between you and them is you're courageous, motivated, energized and enthusiastic. You're doing something about it.

You are ready, willing and able to take the tough steps. So... um... what's in your refrigerator that shouldn't be? What's on your pantry shelf and behind cupboard doors that does not deserve space or accommodation? Pull out a large garbage bag from its handy dispenser and fill it with those items of regret, threat and destruction.

Squirming throughout the process is part of the exercise. These are desperate little demons of appetite and gluttony and self-satisfaction being exorcised from your body. Once the junk and the devilish habits and desires are exposed and eliminated, you're free. The way before you will be less difficult, less dangerous and less exasperating.

Now you can turn your undivided attention to the good things of life: weights, protein and the pursuit of happiness.

Obesity and the Emotions

The link between obesity and the emotions is tight, yet frequently undefined. I've reviewed several books that speak intelligently to the issues of rejection, fear, anger, depression, stress, loneliness and other emotional disturbances and their ties to overeating. The details of each relationship were different, but the themes were similar. The feelings of distress, whether new or chronic, would reach a point where eating was a suitable and temporary relief from the pain; eating and its preparation provided the troubled person with a distraction, a reward, gratification, comfort or a sense of being loved.

Food indulgence was a reaction both automatic and habitual. The subjects ate and ate uncontrollably as life confronted them with its daily dose of conflict. Time passed and the weight mounted slowly but surely. The wild thing is that these disorders are so common and often invisible to the afflicted overeater.

Recommendations by counselors were made to the over-consumers to observe their eating patterns and note those occasions when eating was excessive. Questions were asked. Is it legitimate hunger or do you just plainly and simply eat too much? The exercise often fixed an eat-eat situation by interrupting the activity on the spot or prompted the elimination of the unnecessary eating episodes by the diligent breakdown of a bad habit. Were there abnormal emotions present that triggered the wave of overindulgence?

What transpired in the early impressionable years might in part determine these eating behaviors today. Recognizing and assessing irregular emotional surges can facilitate their dismantling.

The research was broad and deep, and therapy often disclosed the source of overeating. It did not, however, always fix the problem. Work and discipline were still needed to bring about changes.

We are all a little off-balance in that we are not perfect. And not all that appears to be misbehavior is misbehavior or needs analysis; nothing work, planning, discipline and healthy pride can't fix.

My approach to the overweight problem, if it stems directly from excessive eating, is to stop it by establishing an orderly and defined eating plan that feeds one healthfully and often, so hunger is not a haunting problem. It is backed by sufficient exercise to raise the metabolism as muscles grow, calories burn and fat diminishes. The addition of vigorous activity to a physically dormant schedule improves heart and lung power as it fills the mind with purpose, enthusiasm and clear thinking. The combination of eating and exercise is fundamental, and it consistently corrects a bewildered hormonal system.

Exercise, furthermore, redirects and diminishes stress, fills wasted time with the wisdom of physical investment, burns calories as it replaces cravings and relieves the overwhelming guilt of abuse, neglect and domination by food.

Eating and the emotions can be interwoven, and the doctors studying eating disorders and treating suffering patients have their hands full. You're at least aware that these complex conditions exist, if not what to do to combat them. What can you do, here and now, if these subtle conditions afflict you?

I know you have fantastic potential. You can do extraordinary things with the information and conversations you're having at home or in the workplace. You've already started by confronting yourself with the challenges I've put forth. You're considering what I say and its validity and appeal. What about musclebuilding and my references to weight training, protein and the inevitable loss of fat through an honest and admirable way of life? It works. This I know for sure.

Treat what I say less like cold, hard facts that are onerous in the thought and ponderous in the doing. Is that how you prepared for your very first baby steps when your proud parents gawked at you with anticipation day after day many years ago? If you could recall, you'd remember you were giggling, reaching and bouncing around with excited eyes like a lovable little nutso. Enthusiasm unbridled by doubt was your only reference. Not once did you consider how difficult the task could be or how far the distance between you and your beckoning parent. Falling, failing and time and struggle were not obstacles. Think as eagerly and positively about the year to come as you modestly add another to the numbers. Resistance is stressful and fatiguing. Ease into the active lifestyle, unbound and fearless, with that same bright smile and those innocent sparkling eyes. It can happen all over again, over time.

Do you have any hang-ups? Aren't they a drag? Should you dare fight convention and put order into your life, eat right and lift weights, they will grow faint, as surely as the early morning sun replaces the dark of night. It's true, almost poetic.

It's not uncommon in the world of the overweight for the dwellers to think unkindly of themselves, casting a reproving eye on their movements and the space they occupy. Get over it. This is your lot, the boundaries of your life, and here you will remain unless you befriend yourself, pardon yourself of past stumblings and refrain from inflicting further undeserved punishment. Twisted self-affliction damages the goods further, like taking a hammer to the toes of the feet that lost the race. The race is never lost as long as you continue to take another step forward.

What you see is not all there is. Like the hustler selling kitchen tools on late night TV: Wait, there's more!

I love this old world in spite of the violence, disease and politics. Take care of your own backyard and give your kind neighbor a hand when he needs it. Appreciate yourself with due humility for your strengths and be grateful, for as long as you apply your talent and integrity you are making progress. Remember this, ye walking, talking, thinking and feeling miracle: Progress is not only measured in inches and pounds, but also in what is not seen in external, physical structure. Don't fail to calculate the improved health of the internal system, the organs, hormones, enzymes and their interplay, and the subjective models of character in the mind — patience, determination and perseverance. A flood of improvement of far more value than the loss of a pound rushes on beneath the skin.

Don't forget the delight of fulfillment, and the thrill of success.

Perfect, More Perfect, Most Perfect

Perfection exists, but not in mankind. Men, women and children are miracles, but, alas, they are not perfect. Perfection happens, dear friends, though it is not by our doing. I hear a songbird outside my window and his sounds are incredibly clear and true, his repertoire a majestic spontaneous score without affect or fault. He perfectly sings his perfect song. A flower opens its pedals in unseen and silent splendor; its fragrance spreads with the light of the early morning sun, no one to influence its perfect being. There is none among us who views the power of towering mountains raging with deathly shadows and crevices yielding to the tender embrace of billowing heaven-white clouds of cotton who can improve one bit upon their joined presence. Perfection is supernatural.

A thing aware of itself cannot achieve perfection. If nothing else, pride precludes it from gaining the flawless state. Perfection is not for us.

Achieving perfection is a troublesome mission, a paradox, a futility and a lost cause. None of us will ever know the grinning rogue dressed in fine lamb's wool, and in the wake of the undertaking we only become intimate with who and what we are not. How far from the subject can we get? Follow the clever dancer from a distance and observe his fancy footwork, but don't think you can duplicate the artiste de excellence. His steps are far too swift and right.

Now that doesn't mean we shouldn't strive for the faultless excellence, while settling for extraordinary or stupendous, amazing or basic fantastic instead. We must simply keep things in perspective, accept reality, exercise humility and behead the monsters of greed, power and self-centeredness. As for me, I am sufficiently busy and content doing my gracious best — times two or three.

About the quest — seeking perfection — there are pros and cons. Some say of the ambitious venture it disables, stresses, discourages, depresses and defeats. The insatiable hunt interferes with and interrupts one's happy life. I can hear you now, "Oh boy, this is for me; misery is right up my alley. Any promise of diarrhea or severe skin rash?"

We try so hard to improve we wear ourselves out. Nothing we do is enough and we get indigestion. Our mistakes are more evident to us than our successes and we experience limp-shouldered self-doubt and dark-countenance insecurity. Achievement becomes obsessive and activities not directly related to the ever-retreating cause seem trivial, wasteful and irresponsible. We can't sleep. Time off, entertainment and relaxation are off-limits — we can't bear the guilt, or is it the fear, of letting up.

It becomes evident that perfection and the act of pursuing it are obtuse. They paralyze. Crossed eyes and one's tongue hanging out the side of one's mouth — the drool on the chin, the tick in the temple and the muted stammering — are hardly expressions of triumph. Rather than approach the darling quality, the distance increases. The frustration is numbing.

Proponents of the grind see it as a heady lifestyle, challenge-concentrated and energizing. They are a merrily driven mob who take two steps forward, trip on its backside, bounce and thinks it's fun. They get up. They get ahead. Seeking perfection does that for the resilient, non-introspective flesh beaters. Try this and if it doesn't work, try that and if that doesn't work, try something else. Someone or something gets in the way, too bad. Exactly, precisely, absolutely, right on and totally awesome are the colors of their rainbow, at the end of which is perfection.

And where do we fit in, cool musclemakers and weightlifters that we are, strugglers and challengers, seekers and strivers and protein-consuming flesh beaters? We track the beast, have no thought of capturing it and are content. We push, press and relax. Lift, curl and rest. Tug, contract and repair. Hit a set, miss a rep and grow. Ache, fight and persist. Rip, tear and persevere. When hungry, we consume large portions of protein, no sugar and a little cream... and it's back to the venture with passion.

It's not nice to hurt anyone in the process and don't break anything while you're at it.

To bolt on muscle, shear off fat and charge the body with power, we must have our heads screwed on right. Try too hard and expect too much and the adventure is short-lived. Deliberate effort accompanied by moans and groans is required to direct our steps to the gym. It becomes an ugly place where we squander time, evidently, and inflict pain upon ourselves with little evidence of advancement and plenty of failure.

Should we set goals that are too ambitious and far beyond our reach, we will flail as we fail. Our ambition is stifled and our reach shortened. Exercise, should it survive, becomes a perfunctory act to keep the hounds off our scent, the buzzards off our flesh.

Nuts to the dogs and birds. Grasp each day and every workout as if it were your first and last — attitude leads the way and you are getting close, very close. You don't find perfection, but you unearth the gold-hinged hope chest in which it is contained. There are sunrises and sunsets in your training, mountain lake shorelines in autumn colors, warm embraces and sweet kisses, the roar of a Harley and the call of the wild. It's all there within the workout, the exercise, the movement, the action. Honey-soaked pain and drum rhythms of strain, deep sighs of hard work and breath songs of relief; they unite to arouse the senses.

The gym — your training site — is your refuge, a place of encouragement and fulfillment. The gym is where you go to find release, to call out your name at the top of your lungs, to wag your tail, to lick your wounds, to make things happen or to withdraw into your quiet and peaceful turtle shell. Physical pain quenches the emotional pain; physical movement, flowing and steady, eliminates disorder and restores balance; physical power exerted relentlessly charges the body with might; physical action establishes readiness and alertness and physical awareness promotes long life and love.

Here's where some of us go wrong. We count the sets, we count the reps, we count the days, hours and seconds. We count calories and grams of proteins, fats and carbohydrates. We weigh ourselves and take measurements. We stare into the mirror, assess and criticize and wonder. We read, seek advice, listen and compare notes. We become impatient, disappointed and doubtful. We despair. Why does it take so long... been six weeks... is anything happening? I don't look like her... she's, like, perfect... will I ever look like her? No, Bob. What is the perfect formula for me, the ideal scheme, to achieve excellence? I thought I would feel better... I feel worse... I'm a toad. Why bother? I give up! Shoot me.

In a very real sense we find ourselves obsessing over perfection, or rather that version of the enchantment we have created for ourselves: the 400-pound bench and eighteen-inch arms or small waist and cellulite-free legs. They are representative of inspiring goals, but become agents of impossible perfection in the translation and acquisition. Time, and the obstacles it provides in our quest, is exasperating; the day-to-day metamorphous is undetectable, our eye undiscerning and the schemes of attainment are not trusted.

Seek perfection if you must, yet welcome its warm-hearted kin: daily progress, forward motion, sufficient advancement and considerable improvement.

Train hard, and don't accept its illegitimate siblings: second best, hardly noticeable, pretty good, so-so, runner-up, better than nothing and not nearly good enough.

Never quit, and chase away the haunting, wretched demons: couldn't be worse, rotten and miserable, so bad I wanna die and it's the pits.

Gold we sought and fool's gold we gathered; jewels in fine settings appeared in our reach and, instead, dull rhinestones we grasped in our callused palms. The castle of our eye became a tent in the desert, the mansion a shed among the thicket, the palace a shelter of rocks formed on craggy foothills.

Perfection may be dreamed of, hoped for, reached for and sought after. It can be imagined, imitated, pretended, poorly masqueraded and foolishly impersonated. It cannot be acquired. Knock yourself out.

The closest thing to perfection for you and me is soaring freely, flying high with no limits and a three-point landing after another successful training mission.

Personal Safety, National Security

Writing about physical fitness is not unlike writing about personal safety and national security.

A year ago I took a drive to Colorado Springs to get away from the old backyard, see the sights and restore my rusting perspective. I hadn't left the Golden State before I began to relax and observe the fleeting scenery — and my fleeting gasoline; the gauge read empty. The interstate offramp offered a selection of fuels and a wide choice of fast food joints. I pulled into an incongruous cafe that boasted home cooking with a 24-hour breakfast menu and dared them to ruin a ham and cheese omelet.

A family of four walked slowly in my direction and climbed into the booth next to mine. They looked tired, like it was a long hike from the front counter, but they made it. The dad was a gentle guy who, after brief negotiations, ordered the food. Mom fussed in her purse and passed what appeared to be recently snapped photos to the kids, a girl and a boy in their middle teens. Comments were made; smiles and reactions filled the table. They were good people and when the food came I was saddened. I saw what was happening and where these sweet folks were headed. They were silent while they devoured their extra large portions of pasta, pizza, burgers, fries and coke. They ordered dessert and I tried not to look.

The parents were not yet 40, retaining remnants of attractive youth and thirty extra pounds each. The kids were shy and cute and innocent and held fifty too many pounds between them. I believe they all knew it and I wanted to cry for the girl. I paid my bill and glanced at the early evening crowd in the restaurant. There were a lot of large people with forks in their hands and mouths busy at work.

It was enlightening. I'd been involved and content on the California coast for ten years and forgot what people outside my zone looked like. The free-wheeling diversion I had originally planned took on another form. I started to keep mental notes of the human condition now set in my mind. The eating habits, the excess bulk and the lack of muscle tone, the attitude, appearance and the countenance of the men, women, boys and girls around me became my general focus.

I noticed a discomfort within me that I could not define. I was happy, yet discouraged. Life was good, rollercoaster that it is, yet I was depressed. I strive to be positive amid the fray and seldom fail. What was wrong?

Shuffling through the mixture of emotions, it became evident to me that I was sorry for the condition of the majority of folks around me. They were soft, unconditioned and vulnerable. Reasonably convinced I was not assuming a superior or judgmental position, I continued to probe my observations. We've strayed from physical activity and have served up for ourselves a lifestyle of distractions from reality and oversized platters of greasy and sugary food. We're slipping and I'm afraid and appalled. That was the answer to my question, "What's wrong?"

I'm not a crusader and don't I envision myself fighting crime or the larger wrongs of the world. They're not acceptable, but they're inevitable. I leave them to the experts and authorities. However, in the battle against the wrong we do to ourselves physically on a daily basis I take up arms. This is individual, personal and controllable. It's not illogical to say that to the degree we neglect our health and fitness, we neglect one another. Beware lest we become weak, easy prey to resistance, ineffective and apathetic.

Might I present a suggestion? Start with an hour of exercise this week, ten minutes a day, and take Sunday off. Double it by the end of the month and take two days off. Anything goes — get moving... walk, walk and jog, walk with a weighted pack on your back, carry small hand weights and walk up steep hills or climb stairs wherever they can be found along the way. Push the iron.

Sweep your refrigerator, cupboards and counters of junk food.

It's a matter of personal and national security to exercise and to eat right for good. Secure your own borders and support those around you to do the same. When I run for president on the Fitness First ticket, I promise protein on every table and a gym membership for the entire family. Until that day, friends, let's think muscle and might and eat right.

When the thought of another dismal workout threatens your evening, consider the poor character who allows the word "dismal" to enter his mind. He's a lazy oaf, negative in his approach to a life-enhancing engagement. A slug making its way across the broad leaf of a rubber tree plant has more direction, purpose and wit than he. By the end of the day the slug will have accomplished the task he set out to do, relaxed and proud. Slimey. But the dismal character — that may be you, if it isn't already clear — will have retreated, stepped back in time and place and lost precious ground, a sorry mess. More than that, he will have reinforced the negative nature that is slowly gaining a foothold on his life.

Not one thing about a workout is less than exciting, except your attitude toward it. How can a thing that offers so much, provides so much goodness and hope and exhilaration and esteem be dismal? Where's the logic or smart thinking in that appraisal?

Go to the gym and sit on a bench and review the scenery before you. This is where you gain, grow, advance, repair, proceed, improve, heighten, discover, reveal, laugh, love and smile. There's hope in that iron, serenity in that steel, energy in those exercises and rhythm in those movements. Dismal is a word reserved for the devilish things. What you see here is joy, pure joy.

Take a Walk on the Wild Side

Another day in a long stretch of many, how many we don't know and dare not speculate. Let's just assume they go on forever, and while we're at it, pretend they get better and better with practice and devotion each passing day. Be positive, good and wise musclebuilder.

Be positive — the almighty declarative. I'm tired of being positive, aren't you? Don't you ever feel like being downright negative and miserable? It's so much easier. No smile, no bright greeting for this person, no cheery response to that person, no jokes and funny one-liners among your acquaintances and no song in your voice as you say goodbye. I want to hiss today, if it's all the same with you — hiss, snarl and pound my fist on the lifting platform.

Think again, that's a 4-B: Big Bomber Bummer, Bozo. You'll be sorry.

If you go to the gym negative and miserable, you will not get a pump, the last rep or your one-rep max. You won't make any friends; you'll act like a jerk and probably injure yourself. Science and instinct tell us that misery, like stress, is catabolic, and that's where I draw the line. As negativity and misery engender catabolism, positiveness and joy engender anabolism. See how it works? Joy is like protein to musclebuilding and positive thinking is testosterone. Smile and get ripped, laugh and get huge, put on a happy face and bench 450. We can do this. Nay, we will do this! Done!!

There's something to the theory, though I might have overstated and oversimplified it a bit in my enthusiasm, my positive spirit. A negative spirit on the job, in a passing car on the freeway or at the restaurant two tables down, is as plentiful as mud at a rain-drenched construction zone and hard to avoid in a stormy world. The best place to dry off and regain your comfort is the gym, the mud-free zone, where a full-size grin can take an inch off the waist.

I was very serious during the beginning of my workout today; it wasn't any fun and I felt that my teeth-grinding efforts were for naught. That's why I'm obsessing slightly over the negative and the miserable. Serious is good — serious and concentrated, serious and dedicated, serious and intense. But serious and cold, serious and stiff, serious and grim are seriously bad. I wasn't mad, mean or wretched, but no life-giving blood was reaching my finer capillaries, pumping me up like a happy beachball; I felt no tingling heat in them thar repetitions and no electrical charge in the lifts as the weights plowed through the air — plowed like weary old farm horses through rocky, rooted soil. I was a plug stuck in a hole, a punctured, discolored and fuzzless tennis ball wobbling frantically over a torn and sagging net. The thrill was gone.

It was nothing, really, just one of those less-than-perfect, muddy days. I knew it immediately, but insisted on wallowing in the malodorous mire long enough to get stinky and smudged. Kids insist on playing in mud puddles, ya know. Doesn't mean they like it. Though training malaise for me is rare and short-lived, I have experienced it often enough to have concocted a remedy. I rummaged through my handy gym bag and first-aid kit — splints, oxygen, resuscitator, defibrillator, scalpel, *IronMan* magazine — seeking the appropriate medicine, the whatever-feels-good fix 'n' mix, or "insta-fix" for short. I took a meta-phoric slug, which went down smooth and left a pleasant af-tertaste. I'm good, I'm cool, here I come, stand back, look out.

The slug of insta-fix is whatever feels good, sounds ap-pealing, rings a bell, is of interest, stimulates the senses, charges the energy, inspires and is not a cop-out, a deception, a sneaky escape or a cheap evasion.

This is what I did this bleak and despairing day in the safe yet troubled confines of the gym to save my workout from the devil's fiery furnace, the receptacle for training sessions that are not stimulated by the daring and ingenuity, passion and integ-rity of a true believer in muscle and might — a bomber.

Wait, you should know I had already completed my mid-section training, 175 crunches of various affect on a fifteen-degree incline, followed by five sets of 25 reps of incline leg raises, supersetted with hanging leg raises. Pure, uninspired work… had to be done, did it sufficiently.

And I should add that my schedule called for legs: exten-sions, curls, calves, squats and farmer walks. Usually, I greet this particular training session with enthusiasm, squats being a favorite challenge. The reasonably heavy weight on the bar and appropriately slower pace, the limited exercises and the inter-nal thunder are also attractive. However, after months of prime leg workouts, my knees and a hip flexor are getting cranky.

Overtraining is rearing its ugly head, and I wondered in the back of my mind if I would wait until it screamed bloody murder before taking sensible training precautions. I noticed I was approaching the weight rack the past two weeks with trepidation. "Let me at them" was replaced by "Can I go home now?". Bad sign. Today, as I strapped on my lifting belt, I thought I heard "I want my mommy" come from the stereo speaker overhead. There, I heard it again. "No, Draper, that's Aerosmith singing 'You're my baby'." Right! I knew that.

So, as you are fully informed, I did forearms for starters. You're disappointed. I know, far cry from squats, and my fix 'n' mix whatever bears every indication of an authentic cop-out... but I was limping, Coach. I chose my favorite thick bar for the wrist curls, the bent bar for reverse curls and triceps pushdowns with the Stealth Tri-blaster, my short, angled, two-inch thick handle for triceps cable work. This three-part superset is not exactly a rare diversion for me — it's as old and as used as my favorite t-shirts — but it hits the mark every time: smaller muscles at work, unthreatening, agreeable pace, always a gratifying pump without exhausting or fatiguing, exhilarating searing burn without major sacrifice and a pleasing upper body participation and stimulation for free.

I performed five tri-sets of 15 to 20, 8 to 10 and 15 to 20 reps, respectively. No race, but kept moving.

Now here's where I strayed from the norm, boldly stepped away from convention, expressed my freedom, cut loose, unbound myself from society's bonds and went where few men dare to go... into the woman's lockerroom... no, no, no... that was a typo, a slip on the keyboard. Feeling invigorated, reassured and no longer hearing voices from childhood, I let myself wander the premises of the gym. Deltoid work is a problem with many weightlifters after a few years of pushing too much iron, in the wrong direction, without warming up, without practice or without sufficient preparation… without brains, just passion (AKA ego). I'm no exception. Add to that the fall I had that tore something in the infra- and supra-spinatus region (right side, if you must know) and my pressing is abysmal. I cannot do sidearm or forward lateral raises. Rats. I do the lying-on-the-bench things — they're cool — but they torment my elbows occasionally, so I decided to try something else.

Are you ready for this one?

I'm slightly embarrassed, but we're old friends, so I'm gonna tell you what I did and still do. Don't laugh… you'll cause me to withdraw and live with emotional problems the rest of my life. A dysfunctional weightlifter is a frightening sight.

I stand relaxed with a pair of light-weight dumbbells hanging by my sides (start with fives, or five-pound plates will do). This is a swinging movement that requires looseness, some practice and close attention to accomplish the muscular effect. From the standing position take one step forward (left or right, your choice), while at once swinging the dumbbells forward. The step is not completed; it is more of a rocking forward and a rocking back, keeping rhythm with the swinging weighted hands. Step forward and the dumbbells swing forward, rock back and the dumbbells return — with your focused resistance — and past the neutral hanging position to a point behind you. Keep going with unbroken rhythm, rocking forward as the weights move forward and up, and rocking back as the weights — under control — drop back and to the rear. Forward and up with concentric muscle contraction, back and down with eccentric contraction and continue. By Jove, I think you've got it.

It's easy, swinging and rocking, but becomes a challenge as you apply control, as you reach higher with muscle and might in the forward thrust (concentric application) and resist the return of the weights from the peak position (eccentric application), down and to the rearmost position. I do five sets of 15,

12, 10, 10, 10 reps, starting with fifteen pounds and working up in two-and-one-half-pound increments to twenty-five pounds.

Play with this exercise before applying intensity. Discover the action, determine its potential aid or aggravation (damage control), and prepare and condition the mechanics of the shoulder cuff for the work ahead.

I've been working on this top secret for weeks and I like it. Swinging the dumbbells under control becomes a reasonable version of the lateral raise I can no longer perform. Though the absent spinatus/deltoid recruiters prevent total muscle engagement, I get a muscle activity, muscle pump and positive burn I cannot otherwise achieve. Let's see if the exercise affects any substantial shoulder stability or muscle growth — thickness, density, shape, definition or strength — in the next weeks and months.

Drift to a remote corner of the gym and when no one is looking, try the loopy exercise. Tell no one of its origin. We'll keep this physiological breakthrough between us, unless it works, which it will and then, of course, I'll humbly accept credit.

Bombers must be stealthy at all times on all occasions.

Prevention's Sweeter than the Cure

How go your health and fitness pursuits as you cruise the sweet days of your magnificent life? Have you dropped the bodyfat and gained some definition? Did you set a personal record at the gym today? Has the sweat from your lean body formed puddles under the Stairmaster or have you temporarily misplaced your gym bag? I understand. Everyone understands. Truth is, the gym has been less frequented by me these golden days (I'm only saying that to make you feel good) and when I'm there the space around me is thinly occupied. The natives are out in the jungle stirring up sunshine and waves, barbecues, fresh air, beach runs and mountain bike rides. The good life.

We've known each other for ages — we're old friends. May I make a small suggestion, a tiny reminder? My prompting comes from the heart and is more a plea than an imperative. Ladies and gentlemen, boys and girls and you muscle worshippers, lend me your ears. Do not go one week without two workouts. Ever. These can be the thirty minutes that save you from that dreaded muscular disease, The Gap. I shudder as I breach the fearsome subject.

You've heard of The Gap, haven't you: an unmanageable malfunctioning of the disciplinary tract, which leads to the deterioration of the walls of the will? Some folks have been known to succumb to the wretched disorder for months, losing muscle tone and gaining a tire (excuse me) around the middle. Mild discontent, guilt, irritability and sloping shoulders accompany The Gap. Loss of energy and stamina are not uncommon and binge eating has been observed among serious Gap sufferers.

Some seasons pressure us to limit our exercise schemes, and obliging the pressure is natural and right. Summer vacations and winter holidays beg for time off. Be aware and recognize the safe and friendly boundaries of maintenance training and faithfully heed them until the more favorable times when you can blast it with hungry might. Failure to do so leads to despicable consequences. Prevention is easier than the cure.

Alas, the cure demands that you be so sufficiently distressed with yourself that you start your training all over again. Ugh. Don't you hate that? Admonishments precede the undertaking of the bitter cure and recovery is a lonely path overgrown with thistle and thorn. Cures and recoveries are sweet if they are short-lived and infrequent; they teach and reward us with gratefulness.

However, should they recur like a broken spoke on a turning wheel, you can expect that you are not going far. Fail to fix and one by one the spokes buckle, disengage and the wheel collapses.

Nothing personal, but are you losing your spokes, busy enthusiasts? Before tomorrow morning pack your gym bag, prepare your ready-mix pre-workout protein energizer and plan a forty-five-minute re-entry program that gives you ten minutes on the stationary bike, five minutes on the trusty midsection (crunches and leg raises) and thirty big ones on your favorite musclebuilding equipment. Don't get in anybody's way and don't stop. Don't calculate, think much, fuss ever, or talk should a wayward pedestrian wander in your path. You're there to work, to perform, to move as if chasing a loose mouse, but not wanting to catch it. Make this your workout style for the next few weeks to come, which might otherwise be conspicuously absent of exercise and vigor. Random training can develop smart patterns that allow you to move through the gym smartly and smoothly, around the people, wherever you choose with an newly devised, highly sensitive, internal homing mechanism: logical improvisation.

Bench press followed by pulldowns, followed by the dip machine, followed by bentover lateral raises, onto the triceps pulley pushdown and then dumbbell alternate curls (any weight that feels good). Back to the dip machine and the seated lat row, get in a set of dumbbell incline presses. Breathe deeply... you're building momentum. Once again, the bench press combined with the lat pulldowns, triceps machine, and curls... water, always water. Smile, nod, dumbbell alternates (this is the greatest; tomorrow it's legs and deadlifts), triceps pushdowns... one more set... dumbbell inclines.

Gym closes in five minutes, muscle worshipers.

What? Five minutes? I just got here two hours ago. Bench press followed by pulldowns and pullovers.

Why does a person lift weights? Upon first consideration, as a deep thinker, one expects to toss out a few standard responses and move on to the more profound things of the mind. The list of attractions unfold, however, and the question that appeared simple becomes complex.

To build muscle and strength and improve one's health, the classic answer to the simple inquiry, is not nearly sufficient. The one-liner summarizes what lifting the weight does, but only scratches at the surface of why we lift the iron.

We're all different, true, but I'm certain there are reasons mixed with attractions blended with purposes, needs and desires, cures and fixes, neuroses and illusions, pleasures and pains and goals we all share in common. Lifting weights makes nuclear science look like coloring by numbers.

Let me dwell amid the metal. Paint me silver, grey and black.

Ready or Not Here I Come

Throughout my workouts I regularly strap, wrap and cinch myself together to protect this or that and to enable me to outdo my unsupported self. This is quite legitimate as few athletes of any sport perform free of gear of one sort or another for very long. Continual adjustments are required as I move about the equipment in my multi-set fashion, to secure one pair of wraps suitable for one particular exercise and release another that is not. Certain straps need to be bound tightly to enable me to exceed a rebelling joint's limits and quick removal is advisable as circulation is inhibited. Thank heaven for velcro.

My belt is necessary for the overhead load, yet resists my efforts when bent over and pulling at an angle. The wrist strap has been in place too long and my hand is deep blue, swelling and numb. Anybody see my belt? I thought I left it here by the chalk box. Heavy-duty knee wraps take tedious minutes to gather and re-roll while the wrist straps and elbow wraps, looped around my appendages, hang long and loose between sets. I look like the Curse of the Raging Mummy in a tanktop and sneaks.

Supersetting squats with pullovers is engaging as I juggle my belt-cinching and knee-wrapping procedures (wrapping, unwrapping and rolling, re-rolling) for the heavy leg movement with tight wrist strapping and meticulous elbow wrapping (or is it strapping?) for the pullover. A notorious volume trainer, I sometimes carry on like a clown for seven or ten rounds of this act before fatigue, frazzeled nerves and confusion overcome me.

Once I hoisted a loaded Top Squat across my shoulders and backed out of the rack to dig into a hopeful set of four reps... you can do it, Draper. I squinted into the polished mirror before me and noted that my wrists were impenetrably bound in heavy-duty safety-red elastic binding, my bandage-fortified elbows could take a bullet and my absolutely indispensable thick black leather belt lay limply next to my rumpled, totally essential knee wraps on the floor behind me. Something's wrong with this reflection. I was entering a war zone without my armor, standing before a firing squad hands tied behind my back — ready, aim, squat. I got the reps, but it's confusing out there, bombers.

Oh, yeah. I never fail to carry water, a power drink, tissues (got me a runny nose) and a towel on my excursions and on occasion add DMSO, bar-grip expanders and one or two thick handles to the collection. Exhausting. Exasperating. Expensive. I have enough inventory and strategies for a small business venture. One day I will go public.

There are times when I go out to the wilds of the gym floor, um, naked: just my gym clothes and me. What freedom. What courage. What innocence. Truth is, the goofy heap of elastic and velcro-enhanced attractions allows me to train harder and heavier with less risk and less damage and pain and post-workout soreness. I'm getting the hang of it after all these years and I appreciate the on-again, off-again, hand-eye coordination and the pacing mechanism their application provides. They contribute a playful dimension to the sport without resorting to costly aerobic contraptions resembling odd vehicles for space travel. They come in pairs and in colors and are under 20 bucks, belts excluded.

Get crazy. Try 'em. Don't say I didn't warn ya.

Do you imitate or do you devise, develop, modify and improvise your own muscle-building and fat-loss workouts? Following instruction is a legitimate procedure during one's early days of training, but becomes less valuable as you proceed, and obsolete after a year, perhaps six months, of consistent workouts. A year of solid training reflects a serious, committed mind and body craving expression and the instinctive touch.

With the profusion of complicated information floating around like brightly colored hot air balloons, who would think we knew what to do? Lifting weights is, after all, so scientific. Sure. Walking in circles and scratching our heads is scientific if we determine to describe the acts in absurd detail or invent new ways to accompish the ordinary deed. Of course, we would neither go anywhere nor stop the itching for all the confusion we'd create.

Rumbling and Rambling, Raving and Roving

It's clever to know where you're going, but how you get there tells the real story. And though talking in circles might get you nowhere, you cover a lot of unexplored ground in the process. Having properly prefaced my thoughts, let me say I expect you are a deep thinker, of a broad cross-section and not among the failing characters referenced in the paragraphs that follow.

Exercising for health is both simple and easy. It's bright, breezy and liberating. The grim fact that people don't engage in the invigorating act is curious, unacceptable and an alarming display of ignorance and apathy. Tsk.

Exercising to improve one's ability in sports or recreation is hard work and challenging. The athlete, outdoorsman or active person is motivated and inspired. He or she loves life, is energetic and seeks expression through motion and strength.

Exercising to exceed in the sport of weight lifting or body-building is particularly grueling. The means and the end are combined, the act and the purpose joined at the hip. In time they, the training and the goal, become entwined, enmeshed and overlapping. The two become married and inseparable, as one.

You don't lift weights to achieve mass, power and speed one month and start scrimmage the next — tackles, passes, touchdowns and cheerleaders. Oh, no. After a winter with the iron, it's not batting practice in the spring with mitts and bats and balls and beers. The benefits of improved strength and endurance gained from your tough hours in the weight room are not enjoyed while you test your talents and develop your skills on the rings, high bar or the track and field. Uh, uh.

You don't lift weights for a season. You lift weights now, later, again and again, once more, another time, today, tomorrow and the next day. Between workouts you think of working out and you rest, repair, wait, plan, hope and scrutinize — much too much. Then it's back to the iron and steel, sets and reps, monotony and speculation, perseverance, discipline, patience, positve imagining and doubt.

When you're alone doubting, you are usually cranking open yet another can of tuna fish. Doubt either promotes discipline in your diet or causes its collapse. In my experience, if it's not tuna, it's sardines. Water is dessert from the cool shady streams of heaven. The training doesn't end with the strain on the gym floor. It continues with the reign and gain at the dinner table, what you eat, when you eat, how much and why.

It's six meals a day, high protein, low carbs, no Italian pizza, no Danish pastry, no French fries, no Mexican beans, no Chinese rice, no Japanese sake, no German beer, no Russian vodka.

No wonder it's not the choice of sports of the nations. It's a political disaster, discriminating, intolerant and not a lot of laughs. Who can walk the line? At least with other sports you get to play. Somebody throws you a ball, you swing at it with a bat or catch it and run like crazy or you toss it to a giant who jumps and dumps it in a basket, or pass it to a gorilla who grasps it out of thin air and dives over a goal line, rolling and springing to his feet to the delight of coaches, teammates and girls with flailing pompoms. Sometimes you kick the ball or bounce it off your head or steal it or pound the guy who stole it from you. All the time people are cheering and yelling and rooting and laughing. Hey, buddy, over here… I'll have a hotdog and a Bud Light.

In the smelly weight room, you crawl under a bar loaded with immovable iron that clanks and proceed to lift the thing up and down for 5 or 10 repetitions, more if your joints, muscles and oxygen hold out. Then, while no one is looking or caring, you replace the massive mess with a crash, sit up, and like a fool add more weight to the sagging the bar. Time to kill, you sit on the edge of the bench and concentrate intently on the next thrilling expenditure of energy and strength, knowing pain is necessary to achieve advancement in the sport of your dreams.

Five sets of this musclebuilding exercise and you can move on to another and another and another. There's the one where you bend over and lift, and the one where you stand and push, not to mention the one where you sit and pull. How about the one in which you load the big dumb bar on your back and go up and down with your wobbling legs 'till you want to die. That's always good for a few screams from the bleachers. Let's add a few more plates — nickels, dimes, quarters and halves — like they were money and we were rich. Spot me, man, I'm going for a single. If I don't make it, tell my girl I love her.

I remember when I first lifted weights.

The mad pursuit emerged from an active kid who loved to climb trees and jump from their heights. I had a favorite limb from which I chinned, on a favorite tree I called the Monkey Tree. It was my original and personal gym that served me and me alone for years. There were two chairs in the cellar by the coal bin that I placed back to back. I performed thousands, maybe millions of dips between those old splintered chairs when I wasn't chinning on the Monkey Tree. Handstand pushups came later when strength and balance were at my command. Wow.

Then the weights rolled onto the scene: the bar, the plates, the collars, the wrench, the clanging, the improvised exercises and the gravity and the pain. I loved the idea of lifting weights — the height of manhood to a twelve-year-old — but they weren't as much fun or as free as the Monkey Tree or even the dirty old rickety chairs in the cellar by the coal bin. I soon hated the dinky wrench and smashed fingers caught between the cold and noisy plates and the downright uncontrollable heaviness of the mute metal. Sheesh. I'm just a little kid.

I pushed and pulled and from the corner of my eye wondered if anyone cared. No one noticed. Not once did a brother or parent say, "how cool" or "let me try." It was like I was invisible. I was lucky, really. They didn't laugh, nor did they tell me to stop that banging and clanging or get those miserable things out of the house. They secretly liked my crazy preoccupation. The nasty devices were rolled under my bed when not in use, which was next to the beds of my two older brothers. Tight quarters and tight muscles for a squirt.

Nineteen and just married I drove three exits on the New Jersey Turnpike to the Elizabeth Y's closet-size weight room three nights a week. That went over big. Yes, Dear. I soon took a second job (precious daughter on the way) at the Jersey City

228

Vic Tanny's Gym on weekends. That went over big. Yes, Dear. Before a year was over, I moved to California to train at Muscle Beach. My young family followed. That went over big. Yeah, yeah!

In each period after the novelty wore off, the work became Work with a capital double-u, "U" for ugh. Early mornings or after the job, long sessions, pain, sweat, compromise, sacrifice and hard work are the components of commitment. The why, I know now, but didn't then. The twenty-step descent to the floor of the Muscle Beach gym, the Dungeon, held apprehension every morning for three years. I trained six days a week and never missed a beat. Each workout was to exceed the last. The pressure was self-imposed and mounted day after day. The titles came and went. The reps, the sets came and went. The days and nights came and went.

Today it's different.

The sport's become a circus sideshow, an extreme display of cartoon-like bodies, a monster-truck physique exhibition with unwieldy, exaggerated custom crafts surging and bulging in place, ready for the starting flag. I mean, you've got to appreciate the scene. It's wild, rambunctious and jaw-dropping. It's also unbelievable. Where do these guys and gals come from?

These days I enter the gym with relative enthusiasm. It's been this way — joyful, meaningful, fulfilling, entertaining and exhilarating — for years. Once out of the struggling and lonesome developing years things improved considerably. The step from competition took me another rung upward and the sale of the World Gyms in '04 paved the way for training for the fun of it.

Though I train one or two days less to match my age, already acquired muscle and increased need for recuperation, I train harder, with more spirit and with more intention. The expected injuries that accompany time are a nuisance, but have supplied me with unusual focus, training assessment and training affection, gratefulness and humility. I snarl, but I don't bite; that is, I haven't bitten anyone severely. The workout sessions are solid, bold and mighty, for an old hound dog.

I go heavy when I can, when I get the urge, when I feel right, when I need to or when I must. I don't set world records, but I occasionally set a personal record. I'm no longer waiting for the other shoe to drop. I assume it is an anvil, a rusty and battered anvil from an old shed where thick and powerful horses were once shod, rugged hand tools were formed and knurly spikes prepared for early rail lines. I can wait forever.

To go heavy I devise no elaborate program with weight and rep and set progressions based on a six- or eight-week training cycle. The numbers are not recorded and the workout details are not documented. I don't prepare my training, like following dots to form a picture. I go with what I have every workout and take it a little bit further by urgency and God's grace.

Your spirit is your life, and your body the field of venture. Your mind becomes the workhorse. That's why I underline focus, concentration, confidence, continuity, listening and learning moment to moment.

Since deadlifts and squats are a regular part of my regimen (I can push buttons and press pants real good, but not weights) and intensity is my partner, every muscle group and their attachments are sufficiently conditioned and I'm ready to go for a one-rep max whenever the desire gets under my skin. I usually hold out 'till my bodyweight is on the rise and I'm rested. It's risky, but you know how it is. I warm up for five sets of ever-increasing weight and ever-increasing force, regularly assessing the boundaries (courage, will, mood, muscle-under-load endurance, pain variety and pain level, risk factor, relative strength) and get to it when the signals are right. As long as they're right, the anvil will remain high in the sky, hanging and rusting and motionless.

Usually the weight goes up along with my spirits and growth hormone factor and systemic response. If it doesn't, I don't even come close. The whole world, it seems, was hanging on the other end. Next time.

Now, if I want to lose that layer of fat I retain for health and good luck, I apply my secret fourteen-day muscularizing workout and diet plan.

Stay tuned to KBOM for the latest in high-flying adventures and soaring true stories with your host, David, the Bomber.

Anything resembling fact is purely accidental.

It comes down to this: chins and dips, sets and reps, courage and consistency. Throw in plenty of protein and water. You can elaborate on the plan, but beware of confusion. Confusion is the work of the devil and his band of bums. They'd have you thinking lifting weights was a science, beyond man's common sense and the grace of God.

Keep it simple. Replace thinking with feeling, figuring with focusing, considering with concentrating, doubting with doing, worrying with working, whining with winning, concern with curls, research with rows, study with squats, pondering with pressing, losing with living and defeat with delight.

Push that iron. Drink your protein shake. Be nice to your mom.

Some Things Never Change

Preparing instructions based on research and experience, musing and documentation is an unfolding process. That is, you learn new facts, recall ground once covered, arrive at new conclusions, as well as gain reassurance about original ideas. Occasionally, amid the compiling of information, an insight penetrates your being like a flash. Remember the first time you accidentally whistled or really noticed the difference between a boy and a girl? Well, something like that.

Let me recount something I observed while reviewing my early training and diet experimentation. In the early '60s there wasn't a lot in the way of solid facts to follow and I relied on trial and error to set my course — arguably, more direct and less confusing than today, where stacks of sophisticated information abound. I was confronted with the difficult process of gaining bodyweight that begged for muscular size and shape. At six foot and 230 pounds I was seeking to gain twenty pounds of bulk.

I was a recent New Jersey transplant to Santa Monica, California, where the remnants of Muscle Beach resided. The beach scene had receded, but the bodybuilding energy and learning and growing had not. The atom was accelerating. I, by osmosis, took on the training principles that dominated the iron game during this shift from the beach to the Dungeon, the new underground digs for the relocated muscleheads. Powerlifting was infiltrating the ranks of the slick bodybuilders and super-size was gaining popularity. At the same time none of us wanted to sacrifice muscularity; at least, we wanted to retain as much as we could while packing on the pounds. Some things never change.

This was accomplished according to one's own madness, although there were common threads that were woven through the menus of the progressive lifters: high protein and low carbs with the fats being relatively high in that red meat, eggs and milk products played primary roles. Salads were big-time favorites and tuna fish somehow took on an importance similar to that of oxygen. The bad boys carried jugs of water. There were no girls.

Notice the trend being set by the greatest researchers this side of the moon. Protein: high. Fat: moderate. Carbs: low.

I set off to gain weight and get strong while expecting the muscular size to grow according to the big food intake and the intense power-accented bodybuilding regimens. It worked. It took time and hard work, plus patience, discipline and perseverance. These, too, I accumulated and developed along the way.

It was during my recent recollections that I recognized a component of the mass-seeking process that coincidentally matched recent scientific consensus.

Bulking up day in and day out can be as difficult as losing weight. It can be as frustrating and delirious, as disheartening and dull. I eventually, through survival and the need of relief, began a practice of eating with stoic deliberation during the week to serve me and power me through my work and workouts. The hardcore bulking phase came on the weekends when time and relaxation were to be found and smorgasbord specials were in abundance at the best coastal restaurants. I packed in the calories in all shapes and sizes on Saturdays and Sundays. I ate very well, ate until my eyes bulged.

There were additional attributes beyond variety and change of pace. I was exceedingly strong for several days after the bulking phase and capitalized on this in the gym for big and heavy workouts; I was tight and pumped with great satisfaction and had a sense of overall well-being. I did this regularly for three years. Two to three months out of the year when the summer rolled around and competition or photo sessions were in the works, the leaning techniques were installed. I deduced that the weight added throughout the year included a percentage of muscle mass accounting for the increased power, energy and well-being; the pump came from the fuel provided by the carbs and the tightness came from the bloat of bodyweight. The logic, which I shared with my buddies, was reasonably correct on all accounts.

We're getting close to my pea-brain observation. Those diets that interest me today as I see them laid out in book and booklet are the ones that endorse this system of steady, healthy food intake in the balances I instinctively prefer for five days, followed by a heavy loading phase for two days (anything goes). Sound familiar?

The proponents of these diet procedures are doctors and researchers and recognized experts in the musclebuilding and nutritional fields. These gentlemen go further than I in explaining the facts behind the musclebuilding, fat-burning properties of this up-down feeding mechanism. It has been discovered that the hormones intricately involved in muscular growth — testosterone, growth hormone and insulin — are positively impacted by the scheme. These body-shaping and energy-producing hormones can be manipulated by your eating plan to bring about the changes you seek.

What I perceived as bulking up for two days until I was satisfied (couldn't stand further discomfort and bloat) turns out to have been an undeveloped and unheralded version of the popular hormone-adjusting, musclebuilding plans put forth by later diet manipulation experts. I regulated the weekend bulking phase of the diet because I was sure the added quick weight would remain as long-term, insistent fat. This would not do. As suggested by the wise and studious experts, the bulking phase provides a surge of carbs (sugar), thus stimulating insulin production. These in turn cause intracellular glucose loading and cellular hydration, the perfect setting for intense training. The intense training stimulates growth hormone and testosterone levels. We're in paradise.

However, this environment of intense anabolic stimulus has a capricious efficiency span that needs to be individually monitored. The bulking phase is simply overeating and practiced long term and indiscriminately will add fat. It might very well disrupt insulin sensitivity and cause Type 2 diabetes, the disease of the era. It seems we have a world of people practicing the bulking up phase of the plan with notable focus, yet failing to implement regulation and include the intense training. They're in trouble.

I can see a a whole new application for the cattle prod.

Hello. Don't stray. Zigzag your way.

Song of the Whooping Crane

I'm sitting on the end of a bench facing the loaded bar. The loaded bar lying still in the center of the lifting platform is facing me. It's a standoff and neither of us is moving. The fact is the bar will not move unless I move it, one of the rules of the game with which I often have a problem. I chalk up, wrestle with the odds and plan my attack.

The activity on the gym floor is light, a condition that could change momentarily, though I doubt it. The weather is fine, it's early afternoon and the days are lengthening and showing promise. Promise has been missing from the general constitution of daily life lately. Too many in neighborhoods across the lands have come to live on squeezed-dry hope, cheap jokes, sugar and cynicism. I won't mention the fear, anxiety, sadness and anger. Why bother? I reach for my lifting belt and throw it around my waist.

Every step we take is defined by gravity, but the deadlift, pulling the bar before you from the floor to an upright hanging position, takes you inside the physics of the phenomenon and makes you one with it. That's how I think as I approach the silent and lifeless creature, the heartless, breathless, cold and hard thing lying in wait — crouched, really — on the black rubber mat. No one cares, no one notices and a hair dryer blows in the women's lockerroom, the toilet flushes in the men's, the music plays on and the phone rings at the distant front counter.

Move that iron, lift that steel.

There's a lot at stake. Well, not really, it either comes up or it doesn't. What's the big deal? The big deal is this: The bar doesn't come up, your world collapses. That's bad. It comes up and you're a cheerful and generous person who smiles and doesn't yell at people, throw things or glare. That's good.

I'm standing close to the bar and collecting my strengths. Maximum concentration is necessary. Thinking must be crisp and correct. The success of the lift is directly proportionate to the depth of concentration and clarity of thought. I bend at the waist and bend at the knees almost equally and grasp the bar as I shuffle into position. Focus hasn't been fully achieved, but it's imperative that its peak is imminent.

The final tugs on the bar and the setting of the feet and hips allow the critical moment to occur, when the might of the back and the legs is transferred through the arms and hands at the instant command of the brain and its exact and thoroughly positive thoughts. The legs must work hard from a deep starting point and the back must not lag behind unwilling. The tug is often long and slow and never ceasing. Directions are given, adjustments are made. Somewhere between the floor and the full upright stance, the bar seems impossible and foreign, but the motion continues. Strange. No sound in this world. A moment of truth at the speed of light asks if damage is near, do you care, may you continue and then you are erect, fully and completely, and you can hold the loaded bar and breathe and perceive and put it down where it once lay. No glaring today.

I remain bent over as I regain my balance and focal point. An oxygen-deprived brain spins like a top. Back on the planet I remove the belt and consider my next playful step. Water is the drink of the hour and I find myself seated on the same bench alternately sipping and gulping. These are the times I rethink bulking up, getting huge and doing reps with that dinky pile of iron. Never satisfied for long, I catch myself and thank God for the good lift. Wonder if I aroused some growth hormone and will I get a growth spurt in the middle of the night? I'm 100 years old and still greedy. Surely I will be fatigued, especially after the remainder of the workout. I'll knock off some lighter sets for reps and superset them with pullovers to restore the oxygen inventory. Me and my crazy uneducated logic.

A night like this will not be complete without five sets of farmer walks around the gym. Start with 100-pounders and work my way up 125s and go for sixty paces of whatever length in whichever direction is clear. They're a smile. I can move around between sets to maintain a rhythm, sustain the heart rate and maintain my focus. That sitting around between big movements is like waiting for a bus at a country crossroads. Time is muscle.

The gym is beginning to fill up and somebody has an eye on the bench upon which I sit — me and my paraphernalia, a collection of grubby straps, my belt looped over an empty bar on the uprights, a liter of water, a roll of paper towels for my runny nose, foam grips and my personal pair of quick-release collars. Stuff. What would life be without stuff? I gather everything together and, like a gypsy, migrate to a step-box in the corner where no one will venture. The remaining deadlifts will require heart and lungs and good form, but I will not need to dig deep to unbury the ultimate fortitude previously required for a one-rep max. I will be able to think, carefully form the repetitions, define the exertion of the muscles and savor the outpouring of strength. I will breathe hungrily and enjoy the grand pump.

Look out! A bright young lady is heading this way with a 15-pound dumbbell in each hand. She is without expression, and she is walking and lunging the length of the gym with reasonable balance and spectacular determination. Whoop, whoop, whoop… like one of those ungainly birds you see strutting the wet sand at the beach digging for tiny sea creatures with their beaks. She knows she looks funny, but shows no sign of admitting it. I guess if you keep it a secret, no one will notice. She passes by (whoop, whoop) and I smile carefully. Good thing I got my recent most killer deadlift or I'd have said something silly or stuck out my foot (whoops). Looks like a good exercise — glutes, hamstrings and quads pulsing — though I'm sure squats are a lot better. One man's opinion.

I strain with pain to gain, yet not in vain. With the deadlifts behind me and the pullovers under my belt, I prepare for the mighty grip-makers, the trap-tugging, leg-slugging, back-flogging, mind-boggling, sweat-sogging farmer walks. Wondering if I look as terrific as the female athlete who loped by a few minutes ago, I stumble around benches and racks in various directions, neck craning as if I'm lost.

Wow! I'm alive. Every fiber of my body is tingling. Farmer walks are demanding, fatiguing, absolutely basic and almost silly, a stout exercise that challenges at once the whole mind and the whole body. Everything is working and burning and giving out and you can't let go till it's over. These are the times that try the souls of men and women. We must be in shape, alert and hopeful.

There's nothing, absolutely nothing, like the completion of a workout well executed: the relief, the release, the fulfillment, the purge, the surge and the identification with the player next to you who knows what you know — the dear pain, the calming fatigue and the settling muscular throb. Who can buy this, how much is it worth? For the heart and the lungs and the miles of capillaries, it is priceless. The muscles you are born with rejoice and thank you for your care, your thoughtfulness. Energy and endurance are your payment for a job well done. Trim, lean, strong, shapely, youthful — these lovely characteristics are somewhere in your sights. And have you discovered how much fun exercise is? And eating right is a piece of cake... er... stone-ground whole wheat cake with raisins and unsweetened carob frosting.

Smile, be happy. Take her up and cut her loose and go with God.

A workout here and there is valuable when knitting training time together that might otherwise become a gap of such a colossal size that overcoming it would be impossible. So, if life has tossed you in the mixer for a time, grab a workout whenever and wherever you can for as long as you can. Think of these as lifelines that must be gathered and held onto to prevent you from falling into outer space or submerging in a black sea. Don't let go. One day soon you'll live to pump and burn again, happily.

Dungeon Duty

Stepping back in one's memory happens routinely as we step into the future. Automatic references are made to the past, assisting us as we forge ahead. We are no less our past than we are the days before us. They are of the same coin, only claiming different sides. Reminiscing, remembering days gone by can be fun and rewarding, rich with flavor and full of instruction. Alas, old recollections can torture the soul.

Here's a good one from a musty scrapbook:

I set out from my home, an apartment on Copeland Court in Santa Monica, fueled with my 1960s standard pre-workout meal, two rounded tablespoons of defatted and desiccated beef-gland powder and eight ounces of water. It mixed well and went down the throat like everyday dirt. Mmm, mmm, good.

Mud in a tumbler was a ritual I practiced stoically every morning, a sacrifice to the gods of iron and steel. Endurance and rock-hard muscle is what I sought. Mr. America was behind me and the Universe ahead. Whatever it took.

The streets were quiet in the early morning as usual, traffic forty years ago not up to the density and madness of today. I was driving a fire-engine-red Corvette with the top down and the hood of my sweatshirt up. The nip of California fall was in the air. My mind was in limbo as the car rumbled toward the Muscle Beach gym, also known as the Dungeon, and, to some, the tabernacle and the altar.

There was something in the air, a mystery, I could feel it and I didn't know what it was; I didn't want to know and I didn't look. It would reveal itself I was sure. It always did.

Funny thing, I don't ever recall questioning when I was bound for the gym why I was bound for the gym. Never was there room for a wedge to be placed that might separate me from my workout. No mission to accomplish drove me onward, no definitive goal, no exact target, no tangible end result. Weight lifting and building muscle and strength largely and simply defined my life. I worked, worked out, struggled to pay my bills, slept and ate, laughed and cried. I was still a child of the east coast and there ain't nuttin' wrong with that. Room to grow.

No searching for a parking space, I pulled directly in front of the Dungeon's entrance, a pair of faded poster- and graffiti-covered doors hanging crookedly on rusty hinges. They appeared locked and I had the key — lift up firmly on handle and pull vigorously, place rock against door to keep open. No alarm sounded. I was in.

That I was in was not a thrill. It was necessary, it had to be, it was a must, the unspoken rule of my life; now to find my way to the switch box to throw some light on the scene. Throwing some light was not unlike striking a match and lighting a pair of votive candles. I come, I see, I do. Let's get to work.

Everything was there just as the day before. I saw tired Olympic bars, multitudes of scattered plates like families of turtles heading for the sea, and hulking dumbbells stretched out on sagging wooden racks. The dumbbells reminded me of hoods I knew in Jersey who took numbers and worked for the unions, a knarly and troublesome bunch if you didn't know them. What was in the corners darkened by the night, under the hidden stairwells and in that back room where junk was stored and no one goes, I didn't care or wonder. Big spiders and rats, I expected.

Sit ups, leg raises and hyperextensions, intended to strengthen my midsection, gave me comfort in the shadowy stillness. I forced my energy and deep breathing into the dead space, resuscitating it as if it were a languishing ghost. Soon we were both warm bodies and alive. The dried animal glandulars — and youth and determination — were kicking in.

Nobody interrupted the early morning solitude — just the way I liked it, bleak and harsh in the subterranean confines contrasting with the warmth and light at the top of the long narrow staircase. At the far end of the gym the lifting platform beneath the sidewalk skylights beckoned me with a lonely call. The mystery of the early morning was beginning to unfold. I plodded over like a young bull coaxed by mild tugs on his nose ring, a curious and innocent beast sensing a mate waiting in the low brush.

This bull was weighing 245 pounds and eating lots of protein. I did a set of bench presses, as one does to penetrate the cold, wet waters, and the plates clanged loudly. The tranquility was broken. Every cracked wall and dank corner bristled with the reverberations. An unconscious shudder announcing we've begun went through my body. It's time. Lift with all your might till it's over.

I stood on the warped lifting platform, its original geometric flatness rearranged by time, moisture and the thunder of the weights dropping furiously from overhead year after year. I loaded the straightest bar I could find in the creeping morning light. There it lay, an Olympic bar and a forty-five-pounder, a wheel, on each side, 135 pounds.

I did a second set of benches to continue my warm-up. Felt good, real good. Revisiting the platform, I stood over the handsome construction and rolled it forward and back with my foot. Impulsively I bent over, grasped the weight, pulled it to my shoulders and pressed it overhead for reps. I was testing the small mass, kicking tires, squeezing melons at the market. Felt good, real good.

Sitting again at the bench press I felt my gaze return to the platform. It was irresistible. The bench press suddenly seemed one dimensional compared to the overhead press, incomplete, less engaging, not as expressive or interesting. The standing press was tougher and more critical. I found myself adding another wheel to each side. It was Monday, not my favorite day, but I was fresh.

I cleaned the 225, pressed it for two reps and returned it to its place on the hard rubber mats, a worthy hoist offering an invitation to do more.

I'd done bentover rows seriously, heavy reverse curls regularly and my benches weren't bad, but I wasn't real familiar with overhead pressing. You might say this was the beginning. I was now circling the gym floor with my belt in hand, searching for chalk. In the Dungeon chalk was stashed out of sight by the hardcore who liked the white-powder ritual and needed the gripping advantage. I slid a 25 on each side, made the appropriate clang and locked the weight in place with thick collars. I squinted at the pile like it was trouble and resumed my hunt. The floor remained empty, grey replaced the blackness and I was hot with sweat and cold with its evaporation.

I confronted the well-balanced and thickening heap of iron with respect, my attitude taking on the gravity of the weight before me. The objective was to move the weight to my shoulders in one sudden surge of power, make some quick and sure adjustments and press the mass steadily overhead till the arms were locked and the torso stable and upright — hold it for a couple of seconds and return it to the platform sensibly. I'd practiced this procedure half a dozen times earlier in the spring with less weight and less intensity. No problem. I was younger then and it was less important than now.

Deep breath, grasp, clean and press. Job done well with the arms reaching and the weight close to the sky. I hear the sound of life in the distance, a figure doing chins a mile away. The day has begun.

I know what I have to do. Off comes the quarter and on goes another 45. The plates are made tight with a rumble one side at a time, the heavy collars are locked in place and the bar is brushed with chalk. I tug on the mass for good measure and turn to the process of preparing and psyching for the battle: belt, pacing, standing, considering and chalking. Self consciousness is fought, doubt is beaten off, extraneous thoughts are eliminated and energy is focused, these the toughest aspects of the battle. Seeking a culmination of all that is positive and enthusiastic and good and right, I bend over to do it again.

This, the lifting of an impossible weight on a bar, is not something you repeat. Each time is the first time, if it is any good. The procedures have a sameness and continuity about them — position the body, bend, grasp, clean, press and return — but the fury between each step is always new, spontaneous and redefining. Man against steel, steel against man, man against himself. We've got our hands full — we're a crowd.

Ignorance is bliss. No experience, no practice, no technique, few successes and few failures, no spectators, no competitors, no witnesses. The loaded bar and a lone figure, neither a container of deep thought or complex issues. Chalked hands to the bar, gripping and re-gripping, tugging, rolling and feeling. Breaths are negotiated and coordinated, the legs are set, the back is positioned, the arms extended and the daring is gathered. Speeding time slows, wild thoughts cease and power explodes. Something gives.

I did it with back-breaking fullness. I staggered briefly after the clean, my legs remained locked as I pressed and, yes, I leaned like an oak in high winds, but I did not stall or jerk or otherwise falter. I stood and reached and reached and stood for blinding seconds before lowering the weight, letting it go a foot from its resting place.

When you're alone after a remarkable success, satisfaction and gratefulness whirl in your mind with no place to go. They were self-contained, while colorful flashes and mad sounds of rushing filled my head and a wonderful ache flooded my throbbing body. I did it, I whispered with an insufficient shrug: recuperate, oxygenize.

I was leaning on my arms, breathing smoothly and staring at my recently acquired soul mate, 315 pounds of steel, when someone called out from the center of the gym floor. I turned and there was Jack Hughes, a wiry lifter from a generation gone by and now a coach and judge of powerlifting and Olympic lifting contests on the coast. "Good lift, Draper," he said, "don't see too many guys pressing 325 at 7 o'clock on a Monday morning."

I thanked him without pretension, being a very young member of a very old club. I also pointed out I had 315 pounds on the bar. He pointed out I had 325 on the bar and hadn't accounted for the ten pounds of lock-tight collars. He left, and I did it again.

True stories don't grow on trees. Today I couldn't roll 325 pounds across the floor even if I succeeded loading it on a bar in the first place. That doesn't make me a bum, ya know. I'm still a bomber.

Once a bomber, always a bomber. May the wind beneath your wings lift you higher and higher.

The gym is not way across town and the workout is not a heavy, monotonous labor of pain. It's your attitude that's out of town, overbearing and a bore. The gym is where you discover and develop mankind's greatest attributes, and the workout is the wonderful — that is, full of wonder — deed by which you process them.

Where on earth do you come up with your faint point of view? Toys-R-Us, The Roto Rooter Man, K-Mart, Ronald MacDonald?

Sunrise Over Bomber Field

What I know would loosely fill a tea cup and store safely in Aunt Petunia's china closet. If knowledge was power, I couldn't light a match. School wasn't my favorite diversion; I did the minimum time and was free. I escaped. Mistakes, accidents, curiosity, wandering, risking and testing have been my haphazard instructors. What they lack in structure they possess in brutal honesty.

About Draper: "He's not dim, mind you, but he's not the brightest dumbbell on the rack, either." ~*Alfred E. Newman*

While boasting about my intellectual development, might I note that growing older day by day does not add to one's wisdom so much as it adds to the gathering of skin around one's eyes, tris and kneecaps? I don't mind, really, though on some days I consider designing a Bomber Makeover Kit. It would include a box cutter, needle and thread, a bottle of Mercurochrome and assorted Band-Aids. Possibly instructions.

I couldn't be happier with the courses provided by daily living. They are free, abundant and various; you need not stand in line to apply and you are never refused. The singular, one-in-all, all-in-one university accepts everyone. The lessons are often tough, especially when you're dedicated and aspiring. Sadly, participants have been known to hang out, drop out and fail.

At an early age I chose a Harley over a career in nuclear science, accounting or city management. When standing at the crossroads of a life in university classes, dormitories and libraries, I took the sandy path to Muscle Beach. Hollywood knocked on my door and I furiously persisted to execute dumbbell curls in a dungeon. Asked to be a corporate achiever, I turned and positioned myself under the squat bar and knocked out another set.

Today, forty-five years later, I can walk into any gym and with little more than a ten-minute warm-up, proper wrapping and sufficient psychological preparation, do a workout that will shake the cane right out of my arthritic hand. I can hold a conversation with most any ten or twelve-year-old, order a sandwich at a deli, play Old Maid and dial 911. Bragging again, but I've had years of practice.

Enough personal history; allow me to compose a hasty yet instructive list of the Things I've Learned Lately. Ha! This should be quick. Lately would be, say, since age 60, or the past few years of my life. I turn 64 mid-spring, 2006.

A cause for pause: Does that sound old? To teens and the 20-some, the 60s rouse impressions of bent, broken and bewildered. The 30- and 40-some are more understanding and sympathetic, and agree 60-plus is not that old. And the 50-year-olds are quivering in their shorts and looking for hope and encouragement anywhere they can find it — to the 60-year-old, in fact.

The 60s to the 60-year-old is, at last, a precious stretch time with many things to do: fix, save, improve, observe and cherish. It's a truthful time, life is a keeper. To the man and woman experiencing 70 or 80 years, 60 is young. "Oh, to be a kid again," they say.

The Things I've Learned Lately. The list goes something like this:

> *Life is time. Time is quick. Grab it, hold it and it appears to slow down as you catch up. Conversely, ease your grip, let it go and it fades out of sight, as you haplessly sit in regret. Wait for me.*

Don't fall for the lie that you're over the hill, past your prime, or worst of all, an old f__t (I can't bear to say the word out loud). Thinking is believing (I'm 60, I'm old) is an over-statement, but it certainly contributes to the calamity of old age. Renew your mind and renew your body has a nicer ring to it, if you're into adages and cliches. Instead, be real; 60 is 60, another season, another day, another time for faithful blasting.

Sometimes — and sometimes only — it does no harm to recall those days when things were less bright than they are today. Travel back five, ten or twenty years. At 40 I was going downhill fast without brakes: no net, no spotters, no hope, no way. It happens. I know some folks reading these lines who weighed 350 pounds at 30, sat around and ate garbage. What a mess.

We all know others who thought weights were handy heavy objects used to hold stacks of paper in place on breezy days and regarded cold, black cast-iron barbells as grotesque devices from hell.

Get ye behind us, trouble. We observed our plight and pulled on our bootstraps; we grasped the weights, tossed the junk food, practiced fortitude and overcame. Today, at every age, stage and time, the iron is our shield, the workout our fortifier and the gym our refuge and stronghold.

60, like 50, is stacked with promise. This is becoming evident as my drive and efforts have not been thwarted with time. I am, if anything, more capable, and stronger and in better shape in many ways than I was three years ago, five years ago. Why is this, I wondered, and the answer has been shaped by theory and guesswork. I'm not way older simply because I've entered a new decade. To suddenly age is to submit to the notion — the conditioned thought, the commonly accepted belief, ordinary science — that I'm old. I am, after all...gasp... Six-Oh.

Thank God, bombers, we're not the typical product of society. How many of you over 50 and 60 and 70 feel over 35 going on 25, even if only occasionally? Yeah, we have our dings, limitations and aches, our bad days. That's what you get for being fully alive and dancing on the face of the planet. Imagine if you didn't work out and eat right and think like a kid; what a mess you would be.

With careful attention — scrutiny and vigilance and seeking — and consistent effort, you can and will improve. You step backward one day, only to take two steps forward another. Where you lose a toehold, you gain a foothold.

And so it goes. The arms aren't as round and full, but they're harder and more defined. Curling power is down, but the squats and deadlifts are up. The pec development shows no improvement, but the rear deltoids are responding to this specialized training. What you didn't overwork in the past is ready for action in the present. What you did overwork is ready for steady and sufficient stimulation and timely rebuilding. Goodbye heavy bench presses, hello thoughtful dumbbell pressing and cable crossovers. Fret not the losses, the pathways to gain. Focus, invent, discover, improvise, finesse, calculate, modify, seek and find.

About doubt: as usual, don't. Though we know better, there seems to be more about which to doubt. There are not more things; there are just different things. Substitute doubt with tough, uninterrupted pursuit. Be positive, be realistic and don't be dumb; you aren't old, though youth has left the building.

Doubt is not to be confused with honest, well-meaning caution. A little caution and wise consideration go a long way. Doubt, however, seizes our resources, freezes our minds and mortifies our spirits. The body becomes its final victim, limp and powerless. Calculated risk and daring in training is interesting, adventuresome and fun... and most constructive. Recklessness is still reckless, something some of us must recall when loading up the squat bar and bench press. Watch out for your big toe.

Continued meticulous practice with high hopes, AKA relentless bomber training, produces results in more areas than one might expect. Push that iron, don't give up, never give in and press on are the maxims we live by. They're not trite clusters of words to repeat, but powerful commands to bravely enact.

I train smarter and apply growing finesse with the passing time; I learn moment by moment and set by set, exercise by exercise and rep by rep. Due to the increased savvy gained by the years, my tendonitis is circumvented, my structural limitations are extended, the maximum muscle exertion responsible for hypertrophy is enlarged, ability to improvise effective exercise grooves and exercise substitutes is expanded, and my willingness to train when down and my craving to train when up has grown like zeal at a rock concert.

Don't be a fanatic, but do break the chains that bind. Don't let your training desire decrease because you expect your efforts and effectiveness to decrease. Be strong, stay strong. Unless, of course, you have a tummy ache or a boo boo.

> *Giving up the heavy weights for lighter weights to achieve maximum muscle exertion is no big deal. Time and the repeated impact of lifting weights takes its toll and we make appropriate compromises and adjustments to accommodate the rules. Recently acquired injuries, coincidentally accompanied by pain, gain our attention, causing us to learn and re-learn patience, disciplined movement and compromise. They're sharper than us, listen carefully. I'll grumble for a second on occasion, only to reprimand myself for my ungracious and vainglorious attitude.*

Being pleased with and thankful for the achievements gained by hard work and sacrifice is fair pride. Bow inwardly.

Being discouraged and thankless for your compromised ability and slowed progress is vain and pouting pride. You deserve the pain. Press on.

Arrogance is pride in its most devastating form. Kill it before it kills you.

Know the difference between the three, draw the line and stay on the right side where you belong, Captain. Know thyself.

Training must be consistent, but training must have freedom. With the investment of many sound years of exercise, I am able to rely more and more on my instincts to complement my well-programmed training methodologies. Knowing when enough is enough in the process of muscle-loading is increasingly important as age gathers in your gym bag. Too much load is more critical as your long-hammered muscles endure work. I like to take my training to the edge, give it one or two more stunning reps and pull it back before it goes over.

I am more workout-enthusiastic, workout-energetic and workout-hungry when I train four days a week than five or six. I train more intensely and achieve greater muscle overload, which I calculate judiciously, and am, thus, more productive on those glorious days. Swell!

The throbbing muscles are relieved and supported by three smartly placed days of rest and recuperation. Super swell!! I'm getting a pump thinking about it.

Who says you're too old to lift weights once you're outta high school or college or your mid-40s and 50s? Like kids and bombers, training is forever.

Grab some air and fly high.

Training is a long-term investment. You train today and it — the workout, the sets and reps and tonnage moved — is deposited in the appropriate on-body account for future benefits. The interest rate is good (amazing, really), the integrity is undeniable, the commodity is priceless and the demand continuous. I am just a dabbler in the market, but I guarantee there is absolutely no risk involved. You cannot lose, you can only gain and there are daily perks according to your participation. They include decreased apathy and stress and increased enthusiasm and fulfillment.

Besides living longer and with quality of life, you get to walk around with big arms, brute strength and the confidence of a grizzly bear. Buy. Buy. Buy.

Tell it to the Tooth Fairy

Oh, my, it's morning already. Time to rise and shine, up 'n' at 'em, the early bird gets the worm, today is the first day of the rest of your life and all that stuff.

The average person wakes up, stretches, splashes around in the bathroom for ten minutes, has a cup of coffee and a poptart and is off to slug it out with the rest of the world.

The average lifter wakes up, stretches, flexes, extends, reaches, bends and generally considers his mobility, muscle tone or lack thereof. He splashes around and sneaks a few quick peeks in the right bathroom mirror from the precise angle… hmmm… holding water, cut the late-night carbs, bring in the cardio later this month to attack the winter weight… the muscle's there. Time. It's happening. Time and courage. We're gonna do this. Patience, pal, and discipline. Yes!

The pile of pills grows as he prepares his protein shake. The kitchen counter is cluttered with a blender of ice, a jug of low-fat milk, fertile eggs, a bottle of EFAs, protein powder and a banana. He mutters little musclebuilding reminders: Don't forget the creatine and the glucosamine; go for a pump today and maybe a single in the squat if the inflammation is down... better stick two thermogenics in my left front pocket for this afternoon's workout... we'll blast it. Let's see... old brown bag packed with pop-top can of tuna, cooked steak — slice it — and small baked potato in Tupperware, cold quartered vegetables in a baggy and some fresh fruit and a liter of clear water. Keep a bottle of aminos on hand and fill an empty vitamin bottle with protein powder just in case. Gonna be a long day and the muscles must remain in an anabolic environment without providing excess fat-storing calories.

He's ready to hit the road after a cup of coffee and a bran muffin to top the protein shake... and the pills, capsules, nutritional powders and water. "Bye, Sweetheart, love ya, see ya at the gym. Don't forget your chondroitin."

It's worth the effort and what appear to be extra dollars and time, attention and foolishness. Health and strength come at a small price. The cost of sickness and frailty is enormous, too costly to be estimated.

What is the price of a shortened life? Or the value of one that is tired and broken and without vitality, a life that is limited by weakness, immobility, fatigue, a ravished self-image, lack of motivation, purpose and will? It's prison in a free world, solitary confinement.

Let's bust out of this joint.

I must admit I'm a little achy and disoriented lately. Each year is different — events, job, finances, relationships, health, wins and losses, the good and the bad, the steps forward and the steps back. You add them up and what you get is who you are. Maybe I'm getting older? Nah. Maybe it's been a goofy year. Whatever. The condition I'm in — the mood or attitude, the slump or tilt, the chills or sweats — suggests I try something different in my training. What? Not bulking up and going for heavy lifts — too demanding, broad and cumbersome; not leaning down and going for cuts — too demanding, narrow and defined.

The word "demanding" appeared twice and in bright red, yet I like demand in my life. I'll temper it. I'm looking for growth and improvement (yeah, Bomber, tell it to the good fairy) with strain yet less pain. But pain must be accepted, nay, embraced. I'll modify it. For one month I will do what I haven't done for a long time in my training: reduce the weight used and increase the pace — lighter weight, faster tempo, less pain, shorter workout, more pump.

Who can relate? In some movements lowering the weight ten-to-fifteen percent will eliminate (another word for substantially reduce) the strain and pain on the elbow, wrist or shoulder. This replaces the grimace on the face with a glowing smile and allows me to proceed more quickly. Flight, freedom, momentum, thrust and exhilaration define my workout and training misery is defeated.

I know what you're thinking. Sounds kind of submissive for a bomber; replacing light weight for pain, tiptoeing in dainty circles instead of marching forward, prancing rather than galloping, ducking, not slugging. It's only for a month, fighting comrades, like rock and roll, a trial run, a brave stray from the known, a daring and defining rebellion against convention, the risky maneuver of a fearless warrior, a noble experiment in discovery by a selfless leader. And you doubted me. How could you?

You're right. I'm guilty. I'm copping out. But I had to let you know and I feel better for it. Confession — admission of guilt — is good for the soul. It reduces stress and thus reduces cortisol (a catabolic hormone), which reduces catabolism making way for the anabolic environment needed to heal injury and build muscle. I'm headed for the gym, prepared to lower the resistance on each exercise, yet seek training intensity through concentrated, maximum muscular effort with less load on the tender joints and less loathing in the mind. A shorter workout, while intense and all-out, will further contribute to the anti-cortisol campaign. I can't wait to try the scheme, old as the hills though it might be, and reap its reward — a grin if nothing else. I just might recuperate and go super-heavy next month.

This is cool. Perhaps when someone on the gym floor dares to say, "Hi, Dave," my answer won't be, "Buzz off, Jerk."

Shoulders, chest and back today, the toughest workout on my whimpering body, in a single breath goes as follows (with effort reduced from max to eighty-percent max):

Four tri-sets of rope tucks times 30; hanging leg raise times 15; hyperextension times 15, followed by rotator cuff external rotation, five times 25, and internal rotation, five times 25, done with an Exertube. That leads to five supersets of forty-five-degree incline Smith presses times 8 and lat pulldowns times 8 to 10; and onto five supersets of fifteen-degree incline dumbbell presses times 8 and seated lat rows times 10 to 15 (oops, went a little heavy in effort, couldn't help myself).

I'm rolling onto thirty-degree incline flies times 10 for chest, complemented with reverse pec-dec flies times 10 for rear delts and back, and finally a goofy combination of stiffarm cable crossovers times 12 to 15 and walking the dog (farmer walks) around the gym floor.

That's it. Feed me. As usual I drink a protein shake and eat a can of salmon with some cherry tomatoes.

Do you see anything slightly creative or novel about any of the above? Not exactly. The salmom threw you, I'll bet. You're probably thinking, "A lot of work, but it's worth it for the scrumptious meal that follows." Nobody said it was easy, and they didn't say it was exactly sane.

Yes, it's true. I like volume. I like to whittle away with sharp tools, always removing life's daily buildup of debris and pigeon droppings, controlling deterioration and adding form, mass and density where I can, may or might. Low volume, for me, removes the pigeon only, adds mass and stirs my appetite for more... volume.

Another thing: Though the exercises are the same old standards, each is performed with its own tracking uniqueness, resistance emphasis and pace variation. In a sense these individual modifications make the basic oldies brand new. Like an infant learning to walk, he goes from a belly-squirm to a crawl before he stands upright and wobbles. The wobble becomes a step, his step a short walk. When his walk becomes sure, he quickly proceeds to running. In time, with practice and to match his desire, energy and curiosity, he jumps, leaps, twirls and dances. Needs, passions, courage and determination define the rest.

Reach for the sky, pilots. That's heaven up there.

Entertain me, feed me, give me comfort, security and happiness, but, oh, don't make me exert myself. I'll labor for wages because I must, but don't expect me to strain or withhold my appetites in my free time.

Haven't you noticed, don't you see;
I prefer to sit and nibble and watch TV.

The Big Chill

I pulled my truck close to the staircase accessing the rear entry to the gym, gathered my gear, rolled up the windows and locked the doors. This was the new procedure, as some creeps have taken to robbing the local vehicles in broad daylight, relieving hard-working, responsible and none-too-rich gym attendees of their stereos and glove-box belongings. It makes one want to apply his grip (made strong by lifting weights) to the redemptive act of crunching dishonest little bones.

I sat for a moment and gazed at the building's uninspiring backside, every bit as attractive as any industrial structure's parking-lot entrance, and silently said something cynical, like, "Been here before," or "This looks familiar," or "Oh, my aching back."

Thus was the attitude as I dodged raindrops, ascended the short set of stairs to the deck and entered the glass double doors to the humming muscle factory. Familiar, indeed.

Now you might say this bomber sounds a bit stiff around the throttle. Nah! Every day has its tones and shades, curves and angles, that's all. Today's a good day about to become better. This is my general MO: I take a look at the day and what it has to offer, I note my reactions and responses to the options, remind myself it's my job to make it work right, throw in some high hopes and give the mix a good shake.

I take a slug and let the good times roll.

So it's raining, so what? Sow seeds, bombers, that's what. Tis the season for planting. The last of the warm and sunny days are gone and the snug short-sleeve t-shirts displaying our lean might are in the closet, bottom shelf. Yesterday I weighed 226 and I felt like a bull. Mid-August I weighed 226 and I felt like a cow. As the Good Book says, there's a season for everything. Pass the mass.

A year ago I publicly threatened to bulk up, but chickened out. Or, maybe, I ducked out. Whatever. This year I'm repeating the threat, like a grammar school bully looking for attention. It's been a long time since I broke the 230-pound barrier and, if I don't gag, suffer shortness of breath or find myself floating around the gym buoyed up by a built-in fleshy inner tube, loathsome and unsightly, I will give it a go. I'll just toss in some more protein and another can of tuna during the day and boom, zoom... huge!

Diehard muscleheads insist on relentless training. The barren months before us offer a change in pace and approach and expectation, forcing us to modify our routines and methodologies. This is very good; unless compelled to change, we just might remain the same. Assuming adaptive changes we'll forge ahead placing new demands on the body and allowing relief and repair where needed.

266

The mind and spirits welcome the variation as well. You might say they are greedy for it. Adventure defines restless and devoted musclemakers, male and female. Give us unmarked trails and we'll reach the mountain peaks before the others.

How about you, bright eyes? We are of many types. Some of us are even-tempered and like the status quo — steady as she goes and keep the ball rolling; all things come to him who keeps his nose to the grindstone. Progress thrives on sound momentum, certainty and sameness. I understand. This approach matches the mindset of the hard-working, time-thrifty, risk-free and grateful musclebuilder: Do, don't doubt, acquire and be thankful. I love it. Discipline, austerity and frugality, never may they wander, never may they rest.

Of course, it is rest to other types that is absolutely fundamental. Rest rules, rest reverberates. Winter is the season to hibernate, says papa bear to mama bear; we're letting the joints rest. Eat, relax, slow down and burrow into the shelter: football on the TV, apple pie in the oven and holidays around every corner, Thanksgiving, Christmas and New Year's. Celebrate, rejoice and go to the gym on occasion when you get the urge. Hardly anybody there these days, so we're not alone in laying low. We'll inaugurate our exciting extreme-training scheme the first of next year. Absolutely and for sure! Works every time, they say. Never fails, I'm told.

This will not do for us, because, in fact, it does not do. Extended layoffs are the kiss of death. That is, they kiss you and you die. It's that simple. Kiss, smooch, fall over, plunk, dead, gone, forgotten. See how it works? It doesn't work.

This is the big problem many face. How do you continue your training spirit and performance through the upcoming months when there are so many factors working against you; excuses, rationales, weak will, holidays, football?

Short answer: You fight like a dog!

Long answer: First of all — confrontation — you must recognize that a real problem, a large problem, exists and that large problem is the daunting collection of smaller problems. Days are shorter, colder, grayer and less lively; gorging holidays run back to back, daily order turns to daily chaos, everyone submits to wintertime sluggishness and they influence our struggling spirits; heavy clothing conceals our bodies and weighs us down. We tend to naturally gain fatty weight due to the above disruptions, and, though not a proven scientific fact yet, due to an increase in gravity the weights are simply heavier and harder to move in the winter, resulting in less pump, fulfillment and inspiration. And, what's this? Oh, gee, we have the sniffles, the first sign of the flu. I'm aching all over.

Second — reality check — the problem, the large problem, composed of all its miserable smaller problems, must be looked directly in the eye and acknowledged. Get ye behind me, Satan, or I'll use you for deadlifts. My heart, soul and mind are bigger than yours. But I must confess, what cute horns and tail you have, and that red leotard is to die for, you big sis. Now, scram.

Third — courage and convictions — you must determine you will prevail and the nippy winter will not to take you down. This is not the primal courage one displays when confronted with violence or high risk, but the steely courage that's needed to apply disciplines with persistence, to choose the pain to gain over the pleasure of leisure, to seek potency over complacency and to stand tall above and before lying down. Bombers, you know the stuff I'm talking about — the dauntless stuff. The stuff you're made of.

Fourth and finally — confidence and high hopes — you determine a plan to overcome the problem, initiate it and adhere to it and before you know it, the skies are blue and the flowers are blooming and the birds are singing and everybody's happy and you're ripped.

There, nothin' to it.

Maybe I can help you on the fourth and final minor detail of the problem we all face right about now.

Where do we start?

Not discounting the first three steps — owning and acknowledging the dilemma are prerequisites to overcoming it — we must reinforce our need to conquer the tyrant by asking ourselves, "What if we don't? What if we go without attending our training and diet sufficiently, that is, wisely and well?" Good question, and the answers aren't pretty.

Training neglect leads us astray: There's the guilt of disciplines gone south, the embarrassment of buttons and zippers too tight to close entirely, the pain we endure when we witness the scale's display of unacceptable numbers and the obvious loss of precious, hard-earned muscle and strength, energy and endurance. Fat in bunches will surely clog our well-shaped torso and, alas, not too far in the future we'll stand once again on the starting block, anxious and defeated. It's a lonely place and we share it with other uninspired losers. Tell me I'm dreaming and it'll all go away when I open my eyes.

We get the picture, Bomber, thanks. Sounds like *The Bloody Texas Chainsaw Season of Lost Workouts*, or *She Took a Lay-off and Was Eaten by the Jaws of a Squat Rack*. You're demented!

We need a plan, or, as I prefer to call it, a scheme, to carry us through the motley days and months ahead. A plan suggests true order, whereas a scheme is a plan with trap doors and convenient arbitrary entries and exits and room to roam. Batman and Zorro and Robin Hood had schemes. They were fair and clever and winsome — take from the filthy rich and give to the deserving poor, without hurting the good. Their methods were generous, bold and free.

That's what we'll do, sort of. In one big gulp, we'll arrange a loose program — a scheme — to serve our basic needs and give a semblance of order to our plans. We'll take it to the gym regularly where we'll perform it according to our energy, mood, needs and desires, completing the extemporaneous input within a 60- to 90-minute timeframe, again, freely chosen by us, the trustworthy keepers of time and deed. There you have it, troops, our training scheme executed with freedom, fairness and balance, not by the anxious labor of an unyielding plan, to get the job done at any and all cost, good or bad, or not at all. The latter will surely keep you out of the gym whether it's gloomy or nice.

An outline and some hints might put a lamp to the matter, as it does get dark in the recesses of the dungeon gym. I'll allow my mind slosh around like a bucket half-full of warm beer.

• Excuse me for being a bore, but stick to the basics — the top ten exercises for building strong bodies 10,000 ways: bar and dumbbell presses on varying degrees of incline, seated and standing curls with personal finesse, squats, deadlifts and rows accented with cable pulldowns and triceps pushdowns… now you've got it, the essentials.

• You might arrange in your colorful mind a repertoire of handy systems to follow from workout to workout, including single-set training, superset and giant-set training. Throw in some heavy workouts on occasion to stimulate the system, maintain your power and sustain your interest. Permit yourself to think and piece things together workout to workout. It's called creativity, the gentle path to rugged gains.

• I suggest you train no less than three days a week, thereby assuring the sufficiency of the less rigid, more playful workouts. Loose in our approach in no way implies light in intensity. Give the obstinate metal a good tug and a mean toss. Obedience and improvement follow.

• Loose in approach allows no space for coping out, either. "Loose" is the means to get you to the grim gym to do the good deed because you're a disciplined bomber not beyond using a little cunning. That's all. Stand tall before the iron and let your instinctive needs and desires pick and choose the exercises of the day. It's grow time.

• What do you mean you're not ready for this unfettered, unstructured style of training, like you were walking an I-beam high above a barely visible construction zone below? Letting go is safer and more stable than hanging on. You get where you're going faster and you learn more in the act about the task at hand and about yourself. It works. I can do this; I'm strong and courageous, enduring and daring. I'm me.

One needs to be a bomber and apply the "loose" application of exercise, training and working out to survive the Big Chill. Paradoxically, one only becomes a bomber by their application and by enduring the Big Five.

Put your mind to the task, your wings to the wind and your heart to the sky.

Every so often we think more highly of ourselves than we ought. There I am strutting around the gym floor with my chest puffed out and brilliant peacock feathers splayed out from the rear for all to see. I have all the answers, been there, done that and am not only an eyeful, but quite clever as well. Look at me. I catch myself in the mirror and the image is revolting. I won't go into the details; they're too gruesome to mention, like bulging gut, knobby elbows, a rooster's neck and a shinny forehead where a mane once grew. Nobody likes a jerk... not even fellow jerks.

I put a scowl on my face and an imaginary bag over my head and continue to train until my unsightly ego has departed. Could I get my hands on the rascal I would strangle it. Maybe next time — he'll be back.

Lesson: Ego sneaks up on us, blinds us and binds us, makes us look particularly foolish, prevents muscular growth, retards power development, causes us to resort to desperate measures and think unthinkable thoughts, embarrasses us and upsets our friends. Sigh!

What If? Never!

I have an advantage over most in that I've endured more winters of training and a heap of them in bitter cold New Jersey. (I know — such an advantage you don't need.) I plan, while the planning is good, to greet each day no matter how somber and gray with guts and gusto. It's a matter of honest commitment to an attitude as of this moment, now, before the grouch grows long hair and fangs. You know the destructive power of negative thinking, a complaining disposition, a grumpy mentality and a downcast heart. If things with the iron get done, they get done poorly. Patience is slim, focus is a blur, tolerance to pain is fractioned, appreciation for pump and burn is replaced by disappointment and annoyance, and the ethereal distance between mind and muscle broadens.

You become a stranger to the steel. Space between workouts grows and your "ugly" list lengthens to include stress, guilt, personal disapproval, loss of muscle tone, increased fat mass (I'm being creative), fear, introversion, halitosis, schizophrenia, nose picking and nail biting.

Bombers: Given it's in our power to create our attitude and respond to its character, let's seek the high way of gratefulness and enthusiasm and toughness. You know it; you've been there. Look for it, search for it and practice it regularly. Make it habitual, anticipate and reap its fruits. We know what to do, how to do it and why. We're among the tiny percentage of society that is willing and able to climb the steep slopes. Exercise, protein, aerobics, sets, reps, chins and dips are foreign to our neighbor. They, like inhabitants of another world, frighten him and her, yet to us they are dear friends.

Just as we must stay tight in our heavy lifts, so must we stay tight in our temperament, our mental approach to our training, our attitude. We're going to make progress toward our goals through the stiff months ahead. No lost time. We will grow stronger and better when the going is good. We will grow stronger and better when we stumble and fall. Observe, take note, pick yourself up, lick your wounds and be on your way. We press on.

Of course it's a long season ahead and not all of it will be swell. I personally shoot for eight out of ten workouts to be very good — that is, in the range of seven and eight in the scale of one to ten. A couple may be excellent, hitting nine. You know the ones; they're contagious and the whole gym can feel them. The remaining two blasts might register five or six and are acceptable and necessary. Instinct will tell me if I'm pushing myself into an unacceptable, destructive workout and I'll withdraw and take treasured time off. To work out on such a rare day would be cruel and foolish.

The positive approach doesn't necessarily mean a big, toothy smile and a repertoire of uplifting one-liners for the folks on the gym floor. I'm rather fond of serious positivity myself. Grunting and growling can be positive, whereas whining and whimpering cannot. A slight scowl works well, but glaring is forbidden. I often grunt and scowl at the same time while I'm having a wonderful workout. New members, thinking I'm deranged, walk circles around me as I exhibit my peculiar form of training enthusiasm. Alas, they're missing me at my best. Three cheers for a good sense of humor, but keep your jokes short and to the punchline. If I lose my pump listening to your tale, it's not gonna be funny.

I admit that one of my most effective motivators is a sneaky version of cheap negative thinking. I ask myself, "What if I don't work out today?" or "What if I don't eat my tuna?" or "What if I skip the heavy squats?"

I know the questions and I know the answers, yet the prepared scenario, the obvious ruse, has a dramatic effect. The morbid suggestion of each question — defeat — momentarily distorts my body, and I'm relaxed only by the single correct response. Instantly, discomfort is replaced by an absolute confident high. Get ye behind me, horned tempter. Faithfully, inevitably, unmistakably, my pre-fixed answer — Never! — sets me free.

What a relief. It's so easy, it's so rewarding; it's self-perpetuating and exhilarating. It's very, very cool. I thank God.

The person you are is clearly reflected in your weight training. Your workout mirrors your character and personality, your strengths and weaknesses, and your intelligence and understanding. In the gym do you create and originate, concentrate and dedicate, imitate and vegetate, procrastinate and eliminate, flex and boast, assist and share, moan and groan, clutter and clatter, snicker and dicker, bomb and blast, battle and war, snooze and lose?

Who are you, really?

The Supermarket Connection

A question for you, but not about you:

How many people on the street going about their daily business pause to consider their bodies? But for our mind and thoughts, there is nothing more present, necessary and indelible. Our bodies contain all we are, holds us together and transports us about the earth's surface. We, in may ways, are our bodies, and I assume everyone on not infrequent occasions flashes on his or her flesh.

Are they concerned about its shape primarily, what it looks like to them and to others? How well it performs, its condition, strength and durability, do these matters cross their minds? Do they wonder, worry and wince, shrug their shoulders and move on?

I take risk and submit that smiles of contentment are rare among the honest and thoughtful. Feelings of discomfort and inadequacy must periodically seize them as they walk past a reflecting window at the mall and catch themselves offguard. Who they really are looks back in despair, a wide drooping figure lost to its own devices gracelessly pursuing its errant footsteps, or a crooked construction of flesh-covered bone, plump in the middle and soft at the edges. Written within a cloud of thought above the sad character in this cartoon depicting today's dilemma are the words, "Oh, no! Is that really me? I'm not yet 35."

A sad condition, indeed. Neglect is personal rejection.

Moving the couch to make room for the big screen TV reveals more awkward truths. The ensuing struggle between he and the material world is humbling. He stubs his toe, strains his back, pushes, lifts and pulls and nothing moves up or forward, and that includes his opinion of himself.

- Approval by one's peers is limited by approval of one's self.

- Confidence is one's personal security system and requires continual wiring and rewiring, upgrading and attention.

- Well-being engenders cheerfulness, enthusiasm and creativity and the energy and desire that sustains them.

- Responsibility and respect are not free gifts, nor can they be purchased. They are the most precious of possessions gained by wisdom and its application. Dubious personal qualities, they, like the couch and TV, appear to be secured to the floor.

I'm a rusty old bucket of bolts as I cross the parking lot to the supermarket. I see from the colorful banners decorating the windows that the price of shampoo is slashed, feeding the dog is a bargain this week and vodka in half-gallons is cheaper than fresh-squeezed orange juice. Twenty years ago the latter would have been my primary target. Today, straight as an arrow and direct from the gym, my mind is on skirt steak, all I can stuff into two or three of those plastic bags that come in a roll at the end of the meat counter.

The last thing I did before leaving the iron palace was biceps and triceps, not a shower and manicure. My sweats are presentable and, though torn free of a strangling neckline, my t-shirt is not exactly a rag. I mean, I've seen a lot worse at the downtown mall. I'm carrying a little red basket, checking my pockets for my wallet and viewing the aisles for emergency items as I hastily head toward the meat department. I pass the sugarcoated puffed and toasted cereals, the canned vegetables, frozen desserts, beers and wines, the pastry and donut section smelling of lard, and racks of magazines, some advertising 14 days to a shapely and muscular body. There are rows of sweet things in bags, boxes and bins next to stacks of colorful soda pop cans.

Where's the beef?

I'm not alone in this popular food emporium. The whole gang is here all the time it seems, 24/7. The men and women — a cross-section — fill their baskets with lots of stuff resembling real food. I feel like a glutton with my sacks of meat, couple-dozen eggs and bags of red peppers and tomatoes, my favorite vegetables. I notice the difference in supplies chosen by those around me and those chosen by me. As when observing a fellow shopper with five screaming kids grabbing toilet paper off the shelves, tossing them at one another and passersby, and doing wheelies with the shopping carts, I try not to feel superior or condescending or outraged. However, I am relieved.

Someone is looking at me, I can tell. It's a fellow in his 40s carting bread and butter, twenty frozen TV dinners, a bottle of red wine, a quart of soy milk (soy milk?) and one of those crappy info mags. I'm grabbing handfuls of cheap canned tuna for Mugsy and feel compelled to tell the guy they're for my cat, not me, that I eat Dave's gourmet albacore. I realize this is silly — let him think what he wants to think — when I note he's looking at my arms. They may not be great, but they are different, veins and all. The man with the TV dinners also has a delicate pauch and arms like wilted carrot sticks hanging by his sides. "Good stuff, huh," he says. I smile brilliantly, almost apologetically, and nod, "Good stuff."

Moving on I ignore the string of stainless steel dairy coolers, deciding to withdraw milk products from my diet, again. Thick skin and mucus (s'cuz me) are the determining factors in this periodic menu modification. In two weeks they — cottage cheese, milk, cheese and yogurt — will be back on the table. It won't be long before I miss the protein and bulk building ingredients they provide. They're convenient meals and I'll long for the texture and taste. Meat, fish, chicken and broccoli washed down with water gets old fast.

A thirty-something guy and gal are riffling cartons of ice cream looking for an extra special flavor. They stand over a cart with two six-packs (Dos Equis) and a carton of cigarettes (Camels). What? No soy milk? Hot dogs and luncheon meats in cellophane are strewn among bananas and string beans, of all things. Weird. They look at me looking at their basket (I'm caught) and I want to hide or make an excuse for the stunned or sorrowful or horrified or resigned expression on my face. The moment passes and we exit the scene in opposite directions, they without the ice cream. They're still young; there's still hope and I fight the urge to make my plea.

Down this aisle I go with my handbasket too full for further purchases, loop around the cut flowers and small indoor plants, past the pharmacy and, at last, toward the exit lines. What pleasantries have the tabloids to say about the celebrities today? Almost in line I see Mr. and Mrs. Thirty-some pushing their cart brimming with color and variety, the well-buried ice cream in half-gallons peering innocently through the steel mesh. I daydream about introducing myself and offering advice — exercise, eat right, be happy — and they see the light and correct their ways and pass these on to their children and the world is saved. Next thing I know some youngster at the register is asking them if they need help carrying their packages to the car. Not today.

Almost forgot. Bran muffins. I seldom freak out in my eating habits, yet sometimes I lose control. I return to the bakery and scour the pastry section until I find a package of freshly baked bran muffins. I pretend they're still warm, oh boy. Into my overflowing basket they go and I catch myself grinning. Where did all this merchandise come from? I came for skirt steaks and I'm buying the kitchen sink.

Either I'm being paranoid or there's another man glancing my way repeatedly. Security? He's a big guy. Older. Retired cop, maybe. I feel guilty about something, but I'm not sure what. I ate a grape. No. I took every last package of skirt steaks. No. It's the bran muffins. No.

The guy behind me asks if I used to lift weights. I want to drag him out to the parking lot and ask what he means by "used to," but catch myself in the nick of time. This fellow has very long hair and painfully placed decorative stainless steel hardware in unlikely places about his face and neck. A shiny hex-head bolt bobs up and down as he swallows. I blink twice, maybe three times, pass him a card and invite him to the gym, when he gets the urge — exercise, eat right and all that stuff. He blinks. Cool.

Now the older cop type is uncomfortably close in the next line, "15 Items or Less"— Top Cop will not louse up my merry shopping spree, I vow. I have 16 items and wonder where they all came from and which one I can ditch so I can squeeze in the shorter line. This becomes too difficult and I scan the Enquirer instead. Susan Sarandon seems to have had a steamy affair with Yashir Arafat back in '99. Old news.

The older guy grabs me by the shoulder and says in a deep loud voice that reaches the produce department in the far corner of the huge supermarket, "Hey, where'd ya get all the muscles?" Everybody looks at me and they're waiting for an answer. Hardware Head tells him I owned a gym and I can get him a free trial membership if he asks me. Mr. Thirty-something, returning his shopping cart like a good citizen, assures the forming crowd that my big muscles are not from eating ice cream.

Where do they come from? The man of pauch-and-carrot-stick-arm fame rolls on by, his cart half-full of the cheap tuna and bereft of TV dinners. I duck, he ducks, he keeps going.

No, I don't need any help carrying my packages to my car, thank you. Show me the exit and I'm history.

Bombers. The secret is you know the secret. I have discovered nothing new. Train hard and don't miss. Eat right — protein high and sugar low — without starving yourself. Be thankful and happy you know the truth and be confident that it is working for you.

Where do we go from here, iron-hearted, steel-spirited high-flyers? Skyward, of course.

Solid Nutrition, Bold Workouts, Muscular Body

What is the best muscularizing strategy for you?

The perfect candidate for getting ripped is someone who has already established a foundation of large and dense muscle through years of serious training — the guy or gal who's drunk deeply from the well of discipline and gnawed hungrily on the root of persistence. That healthy and well-fed person is equipped to cut loose on a wild change of pace, pick up speed and fly, shed some bulk and let 'er rip.

Ready… dial in the nutrition and prepare to be poured into an angular and defining mold. On your mark… there are compromises to accept and sacrifices to make. Get set… commitment is the key, courage the hand that engages it and resistance and doubt the lock to be undone. Go.

Typical reader reaction: Hold it there, Mister. What compromises, which sacrifices? Getting huge for the last 36 months hasn't exactly been a picnic in the park. Six meals a day, tuna, beef burgers, slippery raw eggs down the hatch... gulp... salads, broccoli... chomp... protein shake... gurgle... squats, deadlifts... groan... jugs of water, creatine... sore muscles, rest, sleep, rest ... tuna and more water... ugh... vitamins... heavy bench presses, singles, doubles, squats... have mercy... more protein, cross-eyed smiles and ponderous shrugs.

In your quest for muscle separation and definition, you are going to sacrifice size. Relax, sit down and put your head between your legs... breathe deeply... you're hyperventilating, experiencing minor shock. Your shirts won't fit as tight around the shoulders and pecs, and your arms will take on the apperance of pipe stems. The inexhaustible power, energy and super pumps you delight in from the extra bodyweight and abundance of food will decrease. Get the man some water; give the girl some air; someone dial 911.

At the same time your jeans are looser around the waist and your sweats are baggier in the butt. She likes that sacrifice. The puffy face gives way to a lean jaw line and an attractive hollow replaces the soft padding beneath the chin. Not a bad compromise for the bloated image you're beginning to project. Lean is very cool. You're seeing veins in the forearms and across the now-distinct, slightly striated deltoids. The biceps really does have two heads, and you notice the outline of a horseshoe on the back of your arm. Ride 'em, cowboy. Hi ho, Silver.

All these new and unusual formations make you want to shave your body, get a tan, throw on a coat of oil... find some good lighting in the corner of the gym before your favorite mirror... when no one's looking, hit a double-overhead biceps pose like that classic shot of Frank Zane backstage at the Mr. Universe in London. Could use a little more oil, and a pump would help.

The best cutting strategy is a combination of gleaning your menu and eating less food, letting the bodyfat fall away. This means continuing the frequent eating, yet eliminating the excess sugary carbs (less fruit, no juice, light-light-light on the pasta, breads and potatoes), plus a medium drop in the fat, while continuing to lean heavily on the protein intake. More chicken and fish and a little less red meat. Milk products other than your protein powder will be the first protein foods to go. Drink water by the buckets as always and eat salads and vegetables by the bushel.

It's up to you to calculate — rather, finesse — your consumption of food. That's just a matter of observing the skin and its tone, the scale and favorite indicators such as the mirror, finger-pinch calibrating telltale areas, the fit of your pants, your general body presence and other similar feelings, and eat accordingly. Tape measures and bodyfat tests, food lists and values can be obstacles too onerous or mind numbing to surmount. Go basic. Have instincts, will travel.

Depending on established muscle density, training understanding, genetics, metabolism, work input, attitude and other variables, everyone will achieve different levels of hardness and muscle delineation through different investments of time. And it is relative: What is muscular to one is simply toned to another, what is toned to one gal is smooth to her training partner. Be realistic and personal; do not compare yourself to the pros or to racehorses.

The target is attainable when tight nutrition and hard-hitting workouts intersect. Recall Bodybuilding 101: Everyone is different, requiring different methods of operation. I give you my method and hope it has a beat you can march to.

Training to the rhythm of a B-52, based on my training today and forty years ago, a quick overview goes something like this:

As your goal is to attain muscle tightness and fine sinewy formation, so do your training and eating habits assume tightness and fine form. In contrast, gaining weight, muscle size and power — not exactly easy achievements — embrace broader margins and looser parameters. It's a wide and burly road of travel.

Getting ripped is a tense, narrow runway with little room for sidestepping. Steady pace and meticulous performance, therefore, are the primary elements of muscularity training.

Sound serious? Relax. Don't freeze up or start sweating. I'm pointing you in the right direction and suggesting you tug gently on the reins. The first rule is to be good to yourself and allow the mind and body to adjust to the new pursuits and changes of action. Given sufficient time, practice and personal consent you will find yourself loving the rearranged workouts and responding to their delightful crispness. Be strong and keep your eye on the premise. Here we go.

I'll bet you think I'm going to recommend supersets. Please. Do you think I have no new strategies, tricks up my sleeeve, no slight of hand?

Right again.

Well, lower my flaps; the skies are darkening and we have a long way to travel. Let's get some rest and pull out when we're fresh and invigorated. Watch the carbs, stay off the sugar. We'll be getting into multi-sets, hitting higher repetitions with less poundage, maintaining a keen, yet unrushed pace with totally focused reps as we command superior control and intensity within the muscle. Heavy and laborious sets and reps for the sake of sets and reps are replaced by preciseness of groove to accentuate muscle resistance and ultimate muscle formation. Don't sweat it; give it a bear hug and a big mushy kiss. Change is grand and loves to be welcomed foolishly.

There. That's all she wrote. Whadya expect?

A pound of flesh when a penny for my thoughts is all you need.

Perspective. I stood before the dumbbell rack mid-point in my workout. I was synchronized, en route from one set of a superset to the next and all systems were go. I deliberately paused to consider the heavy iron implements at knee level before me. Pausing, considering, allowing thought to invade the workout is different than focusing. Continuity is broken, a motion is interrupted, an energy is put on hold while another is initiated. And one reality is replaced by an entirely different one. I insisted for a moment to view the weights as someone else — a foreigner to lifting — might view them. The objects that lay there were scarred, harsh, unattractive, pointless and foolish. They were heavy, painful, hard and unforgiving and uninviting.

The pause was stress-evoking, seemed like a weird eternity and far too long in any one day of a musclehead. I quickly conceded the untrained don't know what they're missing and thrust forward to make up for the time lost.

To Soar Like Eagles

Going through life without a particular purpose is okay. You get by. You don't go anywhere, but the days pass. There's television with sports, pro wrestling, reality shows, infomercials, dramas, sitcoms, news and video games. We have food and drink, real and man-made, fast and home-delivered. There are drugs and there's alcohol. Our wandering attention is captured by the endless dilemmas presented by the news media, the hopes offered by advertisers and the general threat of daily living in a post-9/11 world. Purpose? Who needs, considers or has time for purpose?

Purpose, I might point out, is often interchangeable with goals and motivations and is cousin to incentive and is a reason for living.

We are choked with entertainment and distractions, non-sense and goofiness. I'll just slap on my earphones and listen to some sounds on my iPod while checking out my Palm Pilot. Yo. Mad Monster is playing at the One Hundred Theaters complex at the mall and I can purchase tickets with my credit card over my cell phone.

I notice several dynamics are at work obstructing purpose, the main driving force in a productive and aspiring individual, community and society.

• In today's delirious world, a person can be too distracted to have a purpose.

• He is rendered shallow by the senseless frivolity surrounding him and fails to consider the need for purpose.

• He recognizes the value of purpose, realizes the commitment, dedication and hard work it necessitates and chooses sufficient distractions to avoid its responsibilities.

• The importance of purpose is clear, it is hastily installed, yet, as hard as he tries, he can't sustain its requirements. The lure and clutter of amusements are too demanding and overpowering.

Purpose doesn't have a chance.

Life without purpose is like a hand without a thumb; you can scratch, point, tap, count up to four, but you can't get a grip on anything. You can grasp, clutch and snag, but you can't hold on. And you certainly can't lift weights.

Folks without purpose fall asleep at the wheel, get off at the wrong stop and put their pants on backwards. They get by, they make it through the day, they might even have family and friends and a good-paying job, but beneath the first layer of skin there's styrofoam and shredded paper.

Styrofoam is a modern invention that efficiently replaces real substance; cheap, lightweight, a great filler, it insulates and withstands hot and cold — a perfect substitute for purpose where purpose does not exist or is lacking. And, of course, shredded paper is everywhere and free of cost. I suspect I, myself, have pockets of useless shredded paper. They sure aren't hundred dollar bills.

Occasionally I notice I'm zipping along, yet neither moving forward nor back. I look down and lo and behold, my pants are on backwards. I hate that. Not the Captain of the Bomb Squad, I'm without a compass, adrift in thin air, altitude unknown, zipper to the rear and targetless. Mayday... Mayday...

No panic. It's just a warning, like the blink on the dashboard that indicates the oil is low or seatbelts unbuckled; a painless and appreciated signal to arouse and remind us to be attentive, watch where we're going and what we're doing and why — huge and ripped or lean and mean — if we want to get there.

When purpose wanes, when motivation recedes, when a goal is not in sight, I become restless, sluggish and stale. I, as you, am unlike my video-game, fast-food counterpart and the condition soon becomes evident and unacceptable — it gnaws. Steps must be taken to overcome the stall in my forward movement, my flight, and I look toward my training to amend the minor disaster. I have observed that my personal life and my training are inextricably entwined and fixing one gives health to the other. And the closer I look, the more I'm convinced it's my training that determines the wholesome flow of my life — events, moods, energy and spirits.

Training without purpose is like shopping at the supermarket without a shopping list, an appetite or any memory of what's in the refrigerator or on the shelves at home. You wander the aisles and finally come home with a twenty-five-pound bag of Dog Chow and you don't have a dog. It was on sale.

You know why you go to the gym and eat right. The list's as long as your arm, yet you sometimes forget. Life's like that. It rolls along with ups and downs, through hot and cold, and moves in mysterious cycles. We're eager and joyful and hitting the mark day after day, and then the mark eludes us; we become irritable, withdrawn and careless. (Speak for yourself, Draper). We wonder why we bother. We punch at the air and kick inanimate objects and hiss. Swell. Now we're soft and puffy and the weights feel like they're bolted to the floor. No more veins, pump's gone... Good-bye, cruel world.

But wait: Don't flush away months of training and sacrifice in one jiggle of the handle. We gotta feed the fire within continually. The flickering embers grow cold if we don't review the reasons for our efforts, relive our successes and revive our goals and remember that we're special, sort of.

~ Review takes place in the subconscious regularly — preparation.

~ Reliving our achievements is done occasionally when we feel generous and slightly numb — encouragement.

~ Revival of goals must be done with intention, humility and high hopes at appropriate intervals, and as often as it takes for them to become certain and real — reinforcement.

~ Remember, we know people who don't have goals, never heard of them or made them and forgot them — dead man walking.

Occasionally I have both the Ironman in Los Angeles and the Arnold in Columbus, two three-day bonanzas that drop me smack-dab in the center of the land of muscles we talk about here today. This is the kind of motivation one needs to toss some logs on the fire burning within.

Stand back, here comes a procession of noteworthy muscle creations clad in leather straps, ripped denim, chrome chains and vivid tattoos. It's the Ladies Eastside Weightlifting Club reviewing the booths at the Ironman Expo. Hi, girls. Nice ink. Here comes another impressive cast of muscle characters, not as huge or ripped, but nonetheless awesome. It's the Men's Eastside Weightlifting Club. Howdy, dudes. I like the cutoff jeans, boots, whip and cowboy hat. Head 'em up, move 'em out.

I'm teasing... almost. The excitement of the pro shows is uncontainable and I regard the three-day extravaganzas as goals packed with incentives: getting away, visiting old friends and making new friends, and sharing our philosophy face to face with thousands, observing the crowds of enthusiasts, seeing the march of giant contenders and brushing elbows with celebs.

Not that anyone cares or could tell (you know how it is), but I gotta get in shape for these events: train hard, drop the fat, get huge, get ripped, be strong, get some color, look sharp, healthy, younger and taller — the whole catastrophe. This can be tough in the middle of a rainy winter for a guy nearing 100 who is losing his hair and memory, but it's the best thing that can happen to him — the impossible challenge, purpose.

The Arnold offers the same excitement, but has grown larger than life over the years. Annual trips allow me to demo the Top Squat and other bomber devices I love, and I can talk and take photos along with the mobs of folk urgently slogging by like migrating turtles. I might see the same stars and champions I saw at the Ironman only weeks before.

This is good, lest I didn't believe my eyes the first time.

Yes, it's true. They're real. Not Macy's Day inflatables tethered to slow-moving jeeps.

What will I do to prepare for such shows? I'll will do what I do all the time, only crank up the intensity and grin, as purpose is now spelled with a capital "P" — Purpose.

Your goal, your level of motivation, concentration of incentives, clarity and depth of reasons — your decided purpose — determines your training efficiency and effectiveness and joy. Think "why" before you lift, and lift hard.

Time to rest the wings, bombers. Last one to leave the hangar, douse the lights, would ya?

Tomorrow we fly like eagles.

Why We Do What We Do

I'm at the cliff's edge where I must refrain from outright lies and fantasy to offer anything compelling and remotely related to muscle and might. I'm gettin' thin on topics and information. No one believed me last summer when I professed to build thick forearms eating the bones of stewed turkey drumsticks. And you saw through my inverted chins and hanging dips theory for swift muscle growth and reversing chronic tendonitis. What's left? I mean, why do we lift weights?

Ha! That's it! A worthy subject, original and stimulating. Why do we lift weights? It's the central question before every iron warrior demanding deep contemplation and understanding, yet so obvious that it is overlooked and forgotten — worse, it is neglected. Study the question, answer it and we revive and revitalize our purpose for training. Lord knows we need revival. It is imperative to regularly recall, review and energize our iron-pounding purposes, motives, reasons and goals.

Generally there is more than one reason why we train and the number grows as we think about it and continue our plate-rattling pursuits. The list is provocative, alternatively simple and complex and looks something like this:

Why Do We Lift Weights?

- Get in shape — look good and feel good

- Lose weight

- Build muscle

- Improve health

- Increase energy and endurance

- Be stronger

- Resist injury and illness

- Recover from injury or illness

- Overcome guilt and shame of physical neglect

- Respect and responsibility

- Diversion, sport, fun, entertainment

- Enhance athletic performance

- Attain physical prowess for personal security

- Defeat stress and restlessness

- Make the chores of daily life easier

- Prepare for physique competition

- Seek longevity with quality of life

There's plenty of room for your personal favorites.

Every purpose listed is valid, some overlap and some are quite distinct. Training for them, separately or in combinations, involves lifting iron, sets and reps, work, time and sacrifice. That is the minimum, the bare bones of participation. From there, one's contribution escalates as the purposes grow in significance and in numbers.

What reasons on the list for gripping the steel, pumping the iron, tossing the metal do you most identify with? I'm vain, glutinous, greedy and insecure, therefore, I'm all over the list with the exception of physique competition (been there, done that, plus I'm bashful). My training desires and demands are substantial, thus, loads of sets and reps, work, time and sacrifice are required.

Note: As exercise importance grows, so grow the liabilities. Unpleasantries — frustration, disappointment, fatigue, injury, exercise confusion — mount in direct proportion to training significance, and good ole' life becomes a struggle. Of course, the flipside is attractive, providing muscle and might, vitality and self-control, a good fight and big winnings. A hardy struggle and fighting for good make real men and women. But you knew that.

Let's look at the various weight training purposes — goals — and their combinations to determine the effort and involvement required by the challengers — you and me. This helps us define who we are and reminds us where we're going, why and what we're up to — the essentials we often forget or didn't clearly understand or grasp from the beginning.

The first six reasons on the why-do-we-lift list fall into the same basic category, commonly known as getting in shape. 30 or 40 years ago shaping up was no big deal; you watched what you ate, dropped a few pounds, did some daily exercise, got busy at work and play and took the dog for an evening walk. Today it's a major project. You read six conflicting books on weight loss, deliriously watch what you eat for six months, drop 40 or 50 or 100 pounds, join a gym, share at Weight Watchers, hire a personal trainer, invest in a treadmill and scientifically exercise till you drop and quit.

Most want to get in shape, a small lively group is already physically fit and, big surprise, more than a few don't notice or care.

Who could not care? Are they brain-dead, utterly isolated, completely ignorant, totally unaware, void of any sense of responsibility and without conscience, emotion and wit? Hello, can we say respect? Sloth and thoughtlessness — to what degree in man do they exist?

Easy, Captain. Remember, rage disturbs hormonal functions and triggers catabolism.

Thanks, I needed that.

Here's how I see it. The earth is no place for weaklings. That's not a callous statement, a half-witted generalization, a bias or a politically anal comment. It's a fact. The world as a playpen does not exist. Be prepared; be alert, aware, vigorous and ever-ready. The overweight and under-muscled are vulnerable and show evidence of neglect. The unconditioned are subjects that tire and submit under pressure and load. The disorderly and undisciplined are prisoners who falter and flounder. Where one is weak, the strong must work harder. And these conditions apply at work, during weekend holidays, on the streets and throughout the wonderful struggle known as life. And then there are wars and crimes, in case someone thought I forgot. Who perpetrates and perpetuates those nasty diversions and who fights on the front lines? Relax, bombers, a subject for another gathering of minds.

I have two rudimentary questions for those who are considering the list above: How serious are you about your collective purpose and to what extent will you go to achieve it? The answers should be A) pretty darn serious and, B) to a realistic extent.

Today, fit — in shape — is not the ordinary physical condition of mankind. Fitness, in fact, is a rare, admired and sought-after state requiring commitment, hard work and diligence. No level of fitness comes without a price and, as with diamonds and gold, the more you pay, the more precious and abundant is the possession you acquire. To get in shape, that is, to look and feel good, lose weight, build muscle, improve health, increase energy and endurance and be stronger — one through six on the now-famous list — you must be serious and apply yourself to a realistic extent. Anything less will scratch an itch, but not eliminate a rash.

The pursuit of physical fitness and shaping the body accomplish the goals referenced in the aforementioned outline: stress reduction, improved resistance, meeting personal responsibility and eliminating guilt, increased strength and vitality to accommodate work- and play-loads, development of physical abilities and confidence and long life with a smile, all of which is smartly wrapped up in a sporty, cool diversion.

Why, that's not gluttony or greed, bombers; that's intelligence, practicality, efficacy and instinctive brilliance. Neither is it impossible or overly ambitious; it's just another mountain to climb in a life worth living.

Once the initial weeks of conditioning and familiarity are under control, exercise input and dietary disciplines can be bolstered and the more serious work begins. Menu strictness and order fall into place, wholesome foods replace junk foods, protein replaces sugar, water replaces pop and relaxation and smart eating replace twitching and constant nibbling.

Sufficient aerobic and midsection exercises are installed throughout the week. A whole-body exercise routine is thoughtfully arranged and three or four sets of each exercise are applied with meaningful effort, certainty and the eagerness of a winning athlete. Soon one decides whether wholesome fitness is enough or she wants an hour-glass shape and delicate horseshoe triceps, or he plans to bench 450 with nineteen-inch arms. Necessary arrangements are made.

Some things cannot be hurried. For example, all of the above. Hurrying kills, especially a workout. Patience, on the other hand, soothes the soul and accomplishes its object.

The sharp points hidden in the sticky underbrush of my head-scratching words are these: Go for physical fitness with all you have; it's a priority in the world of wonder and woe, not a choice like some think. It'll save your butt and lead you to a bigger and better and safer life. Develop the foundations one day and one block at a time, and then go for the first floor and the second of upward construction. Build a skyscraper, build a bridge. Use your will, your back, your guts and your mind. That's why you have them: to apply, to grow, to serve and to protect. And you'll look mighty good doing it.

We're all different — flash — but the good road less traveled appeals to the inspired few. Let's take a walk down the seldom-used byway and shoot the breeze.

See the maddening crowd bumper to bumper all in a dither on the highway behind us. Wave pleasantly, say hi.

About training: I dare not lose my pace. Loss of pace is a sign of carelessness, amateurishness, distraction, lack of control, waning interest, fading enthusiasm, laziness and fatigue. You lose pace, you lose drive, momentum, continuity, direction, rhythm, involvement, enthusiasm, flow, focus and fulfillment... sometimes your sanity. The muscles fail to achieve the pump and burn signifying a strong, high-performance training session.

With no pace, you go no place.

Train With Confidence

A recent study by Dr. Boris Finkski of the University of Bragmore indicates that the L-Pyruvate Beta molecule when isolated in temperatures below minus 100 degrees centigrade will crystallize and become unstable. Furthermore, refracturing of the invert molecule at room temperature produces a protein substrate that mimics HGH in laboratory owls. Assuming this study prevails, why can't I get huge arms? I've been lifting weights all summer. Bummer!

One more thing. My accromius sub-scrapula is recruited involuntarily by an impinged neuron folliculae fiber at the base of my brain stem. Does this mean I'll always be shaped like a pear?

Eventually, the essential questions are answered and all that remains is the training. Not that we'll ever know all there is to know, but there comes a time when we know enough to put aside doubt, guesswork and controversy; a time to quiet our minds, collect our energies and work out.

Here's a statement or two worth memorizing: Training with confidence is the only way to train. Enthusiasm and determination will follow like boxcars on a freight train. Confidence, the absence of doubt, is a distillation of hope and faith and knowing. Confidence is the pause between heartbeats.

Confidence by its nature is smart and hardworking. It shovels fuel into the furnace. It is not cocky, conceited or arrogant. It's not stubborn or filled with boast. These are characteristics of something quite the opposite. Confidence is secure.

Doubt, by contrast, is a stop sign in the middle of a flowing river. It's the brakes to the floor before your car gets moving. The only thing to follow doubt is hesitation and apathy — twelve-inch arms and a spare tire.

Confidence is a friendly and contagious spirit that enjoys the company of wonder. Unlike question, which proposes doubt, wonder is something to be graciously sought and fulfilled. Continued active, thoughtful training, concentrated and undistracted, satisfies the wonder. You may never know a thing, but you begin to understand it.

Six weeks or eight weeks of training are miserably lost if you vacillate, wonderfully invested if you trust. Whether your techniques are worthy or not, you are. Trust your efforts and you'll grow. Your footsteps will not be wasted.

Persist, practice form and focus, observe and note for future reference and examination. The process is called molding.

You who are disappointed in your progress, it would be trite for me to say "Don't be" or "Join the club," "Who cares?" or "Get a job". I only recommend that you accept disappointment until you're able to, by dauntless training, replace it with the joy of another workout completed, another purchase of understanding, another grateful step forward.

Building muscle and might builds strong minds and character. Respect and humility come from lifting weights and feeding yourself with care.

Focus, dedication and enthusiasm: the essentials of effective training. Discover them, develop them, never let them rest.

True Adventures Presents: Obesity in America

The Committee (them): "Come in. Have a seat. Do you want anything to drink? Coffee, tea, water?"

Bomb (me, I guess): "I'll stand, thanks, and nothing to drink."

Them: "Fine. It's our understanding that you are the Bomb from New Jersey."

Me: "Yes, well, no, not exactly. I'm the Bomber and not necessarily from New Jersey. I'm the Bomber from, oh, anywhere and everywhere: Peru, even, or Sri Lanka... Detroit, Los Ange..."

Them: "Whatever, wherever. Look, Bomb, we'll be honest with you. Your country is in big trouble and it needs your help — we need your help. Your name has come to us from the CIA, FBI, NSA, IFBB, AAU or one of those elitist organizations. They say you're good, real good — direct, dauntless, instinctive, cold, cunning and ruthless. They say you can get to the heart of things, cut it out, slice it and dice it and serve it up like an appetizer. That's what we need you to do."

Me: "Maybe I will have a seat."

Them: "We are momentarily misunderstood worldwide despite our worthy and honorable intentions and rather than respectful friends, we are surrounded by envious enemies. We are called hypocrites, as if the entire world was not hypocritical. We of the Committee have determined that we — those in this great country — have become too lax in our disciplines and too loose in our ways, which is evidenced by our enlarged individual girth and loss of ideals and personal enthusiasm. We're on the verge of becoming losers whose values are being overwhelmed by our appetites."

Me: "Maybe I will have some water."

Them: "What should we do, Bomb? Please submit your report and recommendations by Wednesday of this week. We ask for cogency of detail steeped with nuance. Do not exceed 1,500 words. Speak to no one. You can do this."

Bomb (I'm thinkin' fast): "Absolutely!"

What could I say, "Absolutely not"?

I pressed past the persuaders and headed for my safe haven, the field of metal, the iron zone, the gym where I do my best thinking. They only gave me a few days to fix the mess. What had to be said and what needed to be done were nothing new, nothing they hadn't heard before. In-your-face, I-don't-see-it solutions, like "train hard and eat right consistently," are worth a ton of gold, yet weigh less than a lungful of fresh air. How to convey those six simple words to gain attention and make them reverberate, echo and boom was the mission before me. As with all dilemmas, the gym of steel held the fix.

The parking lot was familiar, hopeful and empty. My impeccable timing placed me between heavy workout shifts, and for the next hour I would be the best-built and strongest guy in the gym. I would also be the only guy in the gym. Make the most of it, Bomber; spread those lats, flex the tris, strut and sneer. I'm bad! I pulled up an incline bench with a broad view of the gym floor in the least-visited corner where the sun seldom shines. Relieved, I sat and let my mind wander, which is like removing a leash from a bloodhound in a junkyard; I was gone.

The problem was planted in the '60s, began to emerge like a flower in the '70s, gained the appearance of a shrub in the '80s, grew like a weed in the '90s, is spreading like poison ivy today and needs to be pulled up, eradicated with care, certainty and swiftness. The grand population has become soft, deaf and dumb.

By the resourcefulness and technical invention of a creative few, the grateful reception of the consuming masses and the persuasive accommodation of the hungry marketeers, daily living has become less physically demanding than yesterday. Largely, we're slipping into apathy with each new technical advantage, juicy entertainment and intense distraction. We know it. Some deny it, others accept it, too many call it progress, too few care to fix it and the consequences are huge and no one can endure them. Besides becoming dysfunctional, we're losing our individual abilities to physically function effectively — push, pull, lift and move — and protect our neighbor and ourselves.

Weak is a powerful word. We own it.

Weakness of body like a toxic fume enters the mind and penetrates the soul and permeates the emotions while dizzying the spirits. Standing tall is a lost art and standing at all an extreme effort. Though modern medicine moves forward, our ills abound and the ability to look, listen, learn and communicate for many appears to be a struggle. In our advancement we've diminished.

We should have planted robust wild flowers years ago. We could have watered and attended their beauty ever since. "Should have, could have," the belated cry of the prophet in the wilderness. Too late now, blind seer. Where were you when we took phys-ed out of school and replaced it with fast food? Very few people regard his or her body beyond its convenience as a container and vehicle for our mind and thoughts, personality and emotions, spirit and soul. A carry-all with bold identifying letters — ME — on the sides, crammed with our stuff for quick, easy travel.

The flesh-and-blood body is a marvelous, mysterious and magnificent construct given to us upon entry into the world. Some call the collected parts a miracle, a gift. Before too long we realize the unique and fascinating phenomenon requires attention to operate and maintain, and in addition to efficient and delightful, it can be troublesome. With the body arrive countless activities, applications and challenges it is meant to execute, and our concern for it, the living body, is preempted by the need and desire to attend its wondrous deeds. Commonly, we are ineffective in preserving and energizing a vigorous body and often mistreat it as if it were a used car and not our precious, living and breathing, skin-and-bone self. How unbearable is the thought.

What's the most we can get out of the fragile and vulnerable contraption while doing the least possible to preserve and care for it? How far can we take it without breaking it? How badly can we break it and still use it... without pain. This attitude toward the body dominates mankind the world over and it is irresponsible and disrespectful, ignorant and ignoble and almost gruesome. We overfeed it and starve it and fill it with drugs, smoke and alcohol. It is then beaten, bruised and run into the dirt and we worry ourselves to death when it's busted, diseased or ailing. We choke the body, mangle it, use it improperly or don't use it at all. We don't care for it. We fail to exercise it, seldom sooth it and never let it rest, though it passes out on regular intervals.

This almost sadistic nature we display is not sadism at all. It's simpler than that. It is stupid, asinine, clueless, screwed, reckless, negligent and childish. It's disrespectful, dishonorable and irresponsible. It's mean, and for no reason.

Take heart. None of the aforementioned describes you. You are bombers. I tend to generalize when perusing and recapitulating, referencing interchangeably, they, you, us, me, them and I. Yet, I make a point (cruel at times) and maintain a decent percentage of accuracy in my assessments (plus or minus two percent). Athletes, whose actions are thoughtful and motivated, fall into another category and are excused from my accusing analysis. We're cool.

Hmmm. I pause and note: I'm getting nowhere with my concise and urgent solution for the Committee. Hound dogs can't sniff and think at the same time; it's a dog's law. Back to work, tail wagging, ears flopping and nose to the ground.

Now when it comes to improving the body's immediate appearance, we live by completely different standards and apply a range of extensive, expensive tricks. Looks rule. Function suffers while the face is getting a lift — and the chin, and the chest, and the butt. Cosmetics are a billion-dollar industry: lotions and creams, colors and toners, the tweaks and dabs one applies to the skin, eyes, hair and elsewhere. Beautifiers, enhancers, radiants, moisturizers, smoothers, highlighters, volumizers and softeners assemble like the first line of defense on our bathroom shelves and in the cupboards beneath the sink. Only the best for the exterior, while the interior perishes.

And, no, we won't go into the largest growth industry next to fast food, the cosmetic surgery zone. You've heard them all; treatments are cheaper by the dozen: tummy-be-gone, breast-a-minute, the-nose-knows, bye-bye-butt, wrinkles-away, bag-the-sags, never-before-calves, hair-here and so on.

Not exactly the avenue of the weightlifter-musclebuilder, cross-training fitness aficionado or natural athlete, but the knife-and-stitch methodology is becoming trendy and popular and hysterical. As the Brits say, "The world's gone bloody mad."

No cost is spared; no pain, time, effort or principle reserved. Unless, of course, we're considering exercise, eating right and discipline, whereupon extravagance surrenders to miserliness. Our fingers grow white with pinching.

The Committee's appeal: "What should we do?"

The answer is in the iron and steel, ladies and gentlemen, the sets and reps. It's in an abundance of amino acids and an absence of sugar and fries. No more soda, Pop, and a lot less chocolate, Ma'am. Say goodbye to the booze and stop smoking — barbecuing — your throat and lungs while hardening your arteries and narrowing your capillaries.

What's a dumbbell press or a barbell curl, an ab crunch or a leg raise? Walk or jog to your nearest gym and find out. Practice them daily and you are on your way; don't stop and you will arrive.

There's no time to lose and a lifetime to gain. Exercising and eating right are far more fun than dodging the discipline now, and far more sensible than dodging the bullet later.

One day you will have forgotten all about the Committee and will soar with the bombers. It's in your wings.

Twist of Lemon

The last of the tuna was wedged in the curve sweeping the bottom of the pop-top can. I scraped around with a wooden stick used for stirring coffee (somebody stole my fork) and wondered why it was so important I get every last morsel of the smelly, less-than-delectable fish before retiring the container. I'm cheap, I thought. No, that's not it. I'm frugal and can't stand waste. That's true, but nope, that's not it. I realized with little more thought, it was the protein that each fragment represented and the muscle growth that would be lost if I ignored the nugget, or gained if I retrieved and ingested it. I dug deeper and chewed on the stick before tossing the tin in the trash and opening another. I'm rich.

"Draper, does this stuff ever get easier, the weights, I mean?"

Ah, yes. I recognize the growl in the voice and the tone of the mute question. I look up and there's Fred with his loopy white cap from a yard sale perched crookedly on his forehead. My good buddy goes as far back in the iron as I do and pretends to be old and worn out. He's a tough as nails and twice as hard. Yeah, there's rust in the pile of bolts, but it only adds character and color.

"Freddy," I tell him, "you're rich. You're here. You've got the world in your mighty grip. Pull up a chair, pour yourself some water."

I'm sitting on the deck in front of the gym under a giant redwood that grows perceptibly by the day, its roots slowly lifting the recently constructed area skyward. "Hold onto your hat, Fred." He's staring at the tuna, but he's not getting any.

I go on to expand upon my commentary of his being, past, present and future. "It's Friday afternoon in the land of the free, my friend, and you're about to elevate your body with exciting muscle- and power-building exercise. An original musclehead, you've been caring for yourself for 50 years and now you're letting out moans that only come from little old wash-women. The mind is loose and drifting, Fred. Go in there and concentrate on your workout; execute each exercise with precision and intensity, one rep, one set at a time. Allow your thoughts to wander no further than the vision of your goal and the fulfillment that comes with the completion of a high-powered bombing session. Turn your passions toward…"

Amid my raving Fred placed his meaty hands on the round espresso table, leaned forward and said, "You are so boring." He got up, dragging his gym bag toward the front door as I reminded him he was an elite master athlete who, due to his perspicacity, discipline and sacrifice, was not of the ordinary cut, those suffering from obesity, diabetes, cardio-respiratory ailments and shingles.

"Thank God, Freddy. Blast it."

Yeah, we're rich.

Remarkable how generous I am after a two-hour training session, two cans of tuna and a bottle of spring water. Had he approached me three hours ago, I'd have nodded sullenly and warned him I was using that bench, that bar, the platform and not to bother me. What a dope I can be.

That reminds me.

I have a long-overdue stack of queries from people, male and female, of differing ages and various levels of experience with a broad range of training problems. However, upon reading and re-reading them, the underlying dilemma is the same: training frustration because improvements have stopped dead in their tracks; no sign of life, not even a twitch. They are convinced it's their workout or their diet or a combination of the two and they can't untangle the mystery.

One guy wants to gain weight, muscle, of course, and another wants to lose weight, fat, of course. A third wants to get stronger and harder at her current bodyweight. Can you see the predicament? I ask you, what do I suggest? I don't know the parties involved beyond their letter of request; I don't stand before them to determine their structure, sturdiness and skin tone. While asking questions I can't look in their eyes, the windows of perception, to discern their musclebuilding conviction, depth of understanding and willingness to train hard, real hard.

I have only hollow specifics: age, gender, height and weight and an outline of their current eating and training scheme. This is fodder sufficient to make a perfunctory assessment for the average Jane and Joe, but does nothing for the bomber who is about to take a nosedive.

I can make the usual menu recommendations: increase the protein, drop the junk foods and sugars, frequent feedings, supps... been there, done that, thank you.

Training insights? Increase the volume, more basics, more supersets, pyramid... yeah, yeah, yeah.

The bases are covered, but nobody's up at bat. Maybe that's it. I'm confusing the sports... take a wider stance, stay loose in the hips, choke up on the bat and keep your eye on the ball. The answer is not in the training program or eating habits. It's in the heart. It's not in the black and white of principles. It's in the red-hot fire of passion.

The fact is we could make one single nutritional and exercise program to fit all three that would serve them exceedingly well and position them on track toward their urgent destinations. The requirement — the unquestionable necessity, the absolute responsibility — is moving on that track with confidence, high hopes and controlled acceleration. This means up the long grades, along precarious ledges, across deep ravines, through tempest and storm and barren desert heat, all the time pressing on with unwavering zeal, merciless power and pace. Now I'm a frontiersman, Davy Crockett, entreating the traveler to heroism and high spirits as they conquer unknown territories.

Expect much, but no more than you have to give.

This is not a stretch. We are influenced by the abundance of information, choices of exercise (and food) and therefore believe we must need them all and make use of them all... if not all at once, then very soon. Further, the desire for entertainment, the threat of apathy and the submission to monotony has us looking for change frequently, convinced easily by the thin theory that exercise variation promotes growth and prevents muscle staleness.

Why not? Is it possible that trainees fail to maximize an exercise or a routine fully and thus do not achieve the margins of musclebuilding overload it offers, the finer margins that demand muscle adaptation and growth, where none might be found in any manner less intense, less painful and less sacrificial?

Retain a good exercise until it evaporates and you fully absorb it.

Unless we're currently flogged and short of breath, we're quick to agree life is wonderful. Daily it draws us in every direction for responsible service, pursuit and achievement. We endure exhausting yet fascinating trials and occasionally plunge into mysterious adventures. Consider: For those devoting themselves to four hardy sixty-minute workouts a week and correct eating, it is sufficient, quite rewarding, in fact, to gain health and well-being while seeking trimness and conditioning. We are bombers, yet we cannot expect the exotic bodybuilding extras (barndoor lats, ripped pecs, six-pack abs, spider veins, cannonball bis, horseshoe tris) without the devotion of the professional, the genetics of the gifted or the freedom and youth of the ever-ready, pre-career, pre-family and pre-credit-card twenty-year-old.

Do not give up. Trust your iron and steel investment. Crank up the volume and throw out the calculator. Built within and ever-developing are the wily feelers that, given half a chance, will direct us toward our potential.

In all your training you must be the governor. You're in charge of your workout regularity, levels of intensity and focus of performance. Wherever there is a decision to be made within your routine, you make it — for example, adding weight on a strong day or going light on a blue day, when to do your aerobic activity, before your workout, after your workout, on an off day or on the same day at a separate time. It's the live-and-learn principle, which is no different than the-learn-as-you-go precept. Try it. Takes common sense, builds confidence and makes life easier.

None of this training stuff is all that critical at any particular stage. Big-in, big-out vs. little-in, little-out theory. See, I did my homework. Seek counsel, yet grant yourself credit for thoughtfulness, logic and creativity. You're in the sky, bombers, which suggests you have the basics down or they're at your fingertips. We live and die by the basics. What we do with them determines how well we live, how big and lean, strong and quick, long and healthy and how happy and fulfilled.

"You know, Bomber, for a living legend you sure talk in circles. I'm falling asleep here and you are yet to make any sense or tell me something I need to know. I want a smoothie."

Wait… come back… one last reminder: When you discover a treasure, consider its worth, delight in its touch and hold it close. It sparkles and glows only when we keep our eyes on it.

Do not remove your hand from the throttle or your eye from the sky.

Mighty Muscles, Brawny Character

This is not important reading. You will not discover short-cuts to muscular excellence, weight loss, personality transformation or financial stability. This is an extemporaneous rambling, an unfolding of thoughts that occur to me as I forge my way though yet another day. Life is good and wonderful and filled with joy. This is my first impression and enduring description, never to be rescinded. Life is also worrisome, cruel and filled with pain. To the diminishment of its latter distinctions I dedicate my days. I am not unlike you.

I don't resist the notion that all things happen for a purpose; all things are as they are and that they have brought us this day is proof enough of that. The world is perfectly imperfect today. That is, was one thing that happened — a flood, a blaze, a war, a newborn, a moved grain of sand — not to have happened, the world would be different. The perfectly imperfect world we know would not exist as we know it; it would not be. Thus, what has been was meant to be. This is it, this is life. We can only change the course of things by what we do now and the plans we make today and implement from this moment forward. There's hope for this fruit basket, if it wasn't for all the nuts in the world.

So, you and I and our brothers and sisters carry on day by day to survive and live well, laugh and love. In the course of events we notice our own shortcomings and weaknesses, our sins and evil nature. So be it. Keep your eyes open; watch yourself, know you are part of the problem and contribute to its solution.

I only allow myself to think on these impossible things when it's 3:00 o'clock in the morning and my eyes are like quarters staring at the darkened ceiling over my bed. Otherwise, I'm as deep as rain in the desert sand. Why we complicate things, I'll never know.

Well, come to think of it, I do know.

Or, at least, I think I know. Pride. Self-centeredness, mankind's driving force, is simultaneously his most iniquitous nature, faulty beyond all others. Egocentricity is a destructive defect and hides its ugly head from its proprietor. Our overwhelming need to have things our way and resist things any other way is in our bones, a conceited madness convincing us we are first and foremost, the center, numero uno. I deserve, am owed and should have priority, control, abundance and a host of admirable qualities, humility notwithstanding.

The Bible defines man's pride as his underlying sin. The Good Book is full of forewarnings, guidance, preventions and solutions, but we can't go there without a lot of explanation, apology and, ironically, hateful feelings. Thus, I'll dodge the silver bullet and toss around some ideas that come from outer space and mythology, scientific fairytales and the shallow depths of my mind.

"Factual conjecture is worth a thousand pointless words."
-*Phonygeus, 3000 BC*

Curiously, it is self-centeredness — AKA selfishness — that gets me to the gym. And it is within the gym walls, paradoxically, that I modify the damning creature hang-up, the ego, and make it a livable and almost adorable companion. I love the gym because it soothes my soul, my most inner place, as it builds my muscles, my most outer place. The gym entertains me, focuses my mind, rallies my resources, teaches me how to count, how to plan, how to perform and endure and enjoy endless exercises that make me bigger and better, healthier and more resilient, smarter and stronger, faster and more agile, wiser and more patient. You might think I'm about to repeat myself as I tend to do, become redundant and possibly obnoxious, but I resist the temptation.

Oh, wait. Discipline, perseverance, responsibility, respect, modesty, sharing and caring — products of the gym — almost slipped my mind.

Next time you have a picnic, a family reunion, a stockholder's meeting, an old-time revival, a gun show, a bar mitzvah, blues festival, rock concert or wedding ceremony, have it in the gym.

The gym, or any version of a gym, whether it's a heap of weights at the foot of your bed or a chinning bar in your basement or the Y in your neighborhood, is not a temple, and exercise is not a worship. It is not a university complete with courses taught by professors. The gym is just the simplest of places to put your body in action with the mind by its side. Together in harmony they seek and reach, discover and unfold, develop and improve and effect the application of the strong and fine qualities of life that were meant to make you better, perhaps the best.

I can't help myself. Wrong doesn't belong, but there it is, perfect imperfection, staring us in the face at every bend. Sometimes wrong looks like right, and it mystifies me how. Imagine someone crashing a jet aircraft into a most magnificent structure full of people and saying it's right, it is good, Allah be glorified. How and why a handful of whacks for their perverted illusions oppress nations of millions I find impossible to understand and accept; more impossible is that I would join a world that would allow it. Sorry for my humanity, not to be misconstrued for politics, which I hate.

When I'm President, there will be a 110-pound barbell set in every household rec room. The world's crises — crime, violence, immorality, terrorism and such — will be obviated as we shortcut their source: lethargy, physical weakness, lack of discipline, absence of compassion, loss of focus, obesity, poor self-image, and vanishing purpose and inspiration.

There's another wrong gaining notoriety and worth mentioning. Have you not seen, have you not heard? The world at large is becoming large, its individuals, that is. People are getting fatter every day in every way: bottoms, tops, hips, feet, thighs, fingers — the whole body is growing plump. It's no secret — been going gangbusters for at least forty years — though we still use sensitive words to define the catastrophe: weight challenged, mucho weight challenged, mucho grande weight challenged and so on. It's killing us steadily and surely, one by one. Worse, it's the diseases behind the disease that are frightening: apathy, ignorance, chronic gulping, agitated masticating, stuffis mouthosis and whatever.

It goes back to self-centeredness, which you might have suspected is the main warehouse of greed and power and the other human failings we possess in abundance. Look here: In getting rich and to support the economy, the food industry massively advertises their junk foods consisting of sugars, fats and chemicals, addictive by nature, tasty and cheap. Somebody's making big bucks. We, the ninety-nine percent who are hungry and blind and resemble sheep, eat the food and poor substitutes suggested by indoctrination again and again, and we eat it a lot. We eat it to entertain ourselves and distract ourselves from the dull pain of reality. We eat it because we want to please ourselves, our taste buds and appetites, and because it's quick, easy and convenient. No fuss, no mess, just us. In short, we are self-satisfying, lazy and dumb.

There, I said it and I mean it. Shoot me. But before you pull the trigger, I love you, man! I don't wanna die.

Dumb — lazy, powerless and thoughtless — is an unnecessary condition that is undone in the gym, if one chooses to undo it. Dumb grows like a weed and is about as attractive and useful. Dumb grows out of cracks in the concrete wherever dirt collects. The moment you think of going to a gym and exercising, "dumb" is put on notice. The moment you enter the gym's door — bedroom, basement, World or Bud's Gym — and commence exercising, dumb is under attack. Each rep and set, every curl and press, reduces the size and shape of the destructive element. Dumb soon resembles an inconspicuous kernel. Persist, dumb dies and smart is born.

It all has to do with the character qualities that inevitably develop as you develop your muscles and might. Once you initiate and pursue the joy of lifting — engaging the body in exhilarating muscular activity, stretching and extending, flexing and contracting, breathing deeply and pumping the heart — living becomes less resistant and more appealing, larger and more fulfilling. One aspires when one has discipline and perseverance in one's strong hand. Patience makes time and room for a grin and humbleness reaps a smile. Any boastfulness and rudeness struck down by hard training is a good thing and the absence of the rogues allows and contributes to one's admirable makeover.

Discipline begets true training and true training begets discipline. The energetic and enduring cycle goes on. Sound workouts beget resolve and resolve begets sound workouts. Sure as rain. Smart exercise begets fulfillment and so the story goes.

There's more. I don't know anyone who exercises with integrity who doesn't improve his eating habits to complement his efforts. True training begets intelligence and common sense.

No one said it was easy and some overweight folks have an extra difficult problem before them. Their weight is out of control and their chemistry is upside-down. The years of habitual poor eating and overeating and unfriendly genetics have them boxed in and at their wit's end. Double-XL obesity may not be corrected entirely, but it can be stopped, reversed and managed. Early confrontation will remarkably limit the toll obesity takes on one's life and the debilitating sense of no control or lost control will be circumvented. Energy and endurance, strength and muscle tone, lost inches and shed pounds are as addictive as sugar, chocolate even.

Every day is a challenge — the best day, the ordinary day, the sleeper and the one that shakes you to the core. None are the same; they are not predictable and taking them for granted is a grave mistake. One day they're gone, mine, yours, your friend's, your enemy's. The idea is to make the most of each day, every day, sunrise to sunset, without flogging yourself or others. Light a campfire, but don't burn down the forest. Take the elevator to the penthouse, but don't jump from the top to be the first to the bottom. Take the stairs, one step, one day at a time.

If you insist on jumping, bombers, take your chute, practice your emergency procedures and land with aplomb. They're watching us.

Aches and pain, our bodies complain.

We sit back and eat and hope for healing. Instead, the injuries and weaknesses increase and the healing slows to a crawl. We grow soft and smooth and round and old before our time. We perceive ourselves as struggling and aging and slightly miserable; and lo and behold, we become who we think we are.

Inaction is a disease worse than typhoid. We let it happen. We watch with glazed eyes.

Peaks and Valleys and Plateaus

The barbells were neatly arranged and bolted to the floor. The dumbbells were located along the length of the room where the gravity was evidently doubled by electromagnetic force fields or some sort of high-tech gyroscopic gadgetry or perhaps transverse nano-molecular tubing. The pulley systems were tightened down with wrenches to make turning them almost impossible and the various machines were frozen solid by oxidative expansion wherever metal met metal. Nothing moved without great difficulty.

The only reasonable explanation — the gym was rigged, tricked out and tampered with. Not everyone agreed with me as usual, some going so far as to say I was imagining things, hallucinating. Paranoid. Ha! I know when a place is hobbled just to drive me mad. I told a stooped, gray-haired gent behind the counter I knew what they were up to and I'd give them a day to get the gym back together or I'd be back to take it apart. Bloody mad, I was.

He nodded, said, "Si, Senor. Gracias," removed his bandana and wiped his wrinkled brow and moved off to mop the floor with aging resignation. "Adios, Amigo," and zoom, I was outta there.

You ever have a day such as this? The cold iron is weighed in one-ton increments; you strain and the dense steel will not move, not an atom, not a millimeter. You're momentarily stunned. What's this? You're silent and despairing. It's the low before the high, that's what; the valley deep facing the mountain high, the darkness in waiting as the sun prepares to rise. I love it and hate it, the blues that hide the silver lining and the stunning silences between the musical notes and their combined sweet song. I enjoy yet dread the wait, the suspense and the anticipation, the brief forever loss of time that hovers overhead during the down times. Ah, but for hope... there's always hope. This is only a pause, an uncomfortable, airless space followed inevitably by relief and its miraculous power; a beaming resurgence of energy and mighty muscular rebound, the sure upward movement of sinewy hands gripping solid iron, impelled by tried, yet ever-growing spirits.

Rising after a decline is inspiring and triumph after a notion of failure is exhilarating. The weights fly through the air as if propelled by unknown forces, the muscles pump and burn and sing in harmony; the body looks and feels strong and, once well-fed, sleeps restfully at night. Life is grand!

Now what? Up and down we go like yoyos on short strings. Are the ups sufficient, are the downs too much to bear? Is there a balance between the two, is there a difference, or do we find that as we understand the downs and recognize them as part of the advancing whole, the work in progress — that is, you and me, our life of breathing, eating, sleeping and training — they, too, are as necessary, intrinsic and enjoyable as their distinct and glorious counterparts? They, the ups and downs, are inseparable, therefore they are one. And not to enjoy and appreciate the down moments, the less-than-inspiring lengths of our life, is to resist them and cause friction and stress, and obstruct continuity, and, specifically, our muscle repair and growth.

Keep in mind, musclebuilders, as our muscles struggle to grow, so do our spirits, hopes and dreams. The yoyo continues its up and down action, a testing playfulness, exhibiting tricks by the skilled, lightening speed by the practiced and around-the-world loopty-loops by the risky and lucky.

It's clear — or not — that I have something to say, but have not yet decided what it is or how to say it. Listen. Building muscle takes time, hard work and consistency through good and bad. You can never give up or give in. You grow according to your input and genetics, knowledge and understanding. Where you are denied in one area, you excel in another, and reach for the potential with which you are graced. Be grateful, I'm reminded to say. Good health and function and courage are priceless. Not every being has what it takes, cannot and never will.

I talk with people who have trained in the past, let go and want more than anything to restore the habit and reclaim the good-time feelings. How to start is obvious: Join a gym and hop right in. Straighten out the diet and replace the junk with protein and vitamins. It'll take time, adjustment and probably be painful at first. So what? Nothing can waste time and hurt more than being out of shape. Jump in there with all fours and make up for the careless years gone by. Lose the gut, ya mutt. Resusitate your spirits and re-energize your mind. The high is exhilarating. Time to dig up your buried treasure of enthusiasm and spend it abundantly, dear friends. And, oh yeah, your class reunion is a month away.

Enthusiasm is like a fuse. Something lights it — inspiration, a dare, a threat, an impending class reunion — and it sparkles, hisses and races across a safe distance to the dynamite, and goes out when the charge goes puff. The workout program, the training scheme, is like the charge of dynamite. It's gotta be just enough to do the job, packed right, have plenty of energy and force, but not so much that it does damage rather than acting constructively. A small bang is dull and disappointing; a big bang can knock one's socks off, send a gym bag to the moon and convince an out-of-shape person none of this was a very good idea.

Can you believe it? Wrong thinking. The best thoughts have had since deciding not to do drugs, smoke, drink or rob banks, and there are doubts. Nope, sorry, no way. This won't do, Chief.

We need a simple concoction of exercise, food and discipline to get the job one. One's personality, physical condition, lifestyle and daily routine are to be considered, but number one, numero uno, is get the job done.

Don't push so hard that you push yourself over the edge; don't expect so much that you live in four walls of disappointment, and don't ever, ever stop, not for a heartbeat. This stuff works. Exercise and eating right always work. Besides, they never fail. Forget the details, remember the solid truth. Age doesn't matter. Got a pulse; this stuff works.

It's the journey, the road along the way; it's the flight, the wind beneath your wings; it's the sets and reps, the pump and the burn. Dream on, but not while you're pushing the iron and lifting the steel. Around the corner, over the next rise and beyond the blue horizon are the joys and pursuits of tomorrow.

I hear the roar of aircraft streaking the skies overhead. That's us, bombers, doing what we do best — training hard, being strong.

Tough; anything that's tough sounds rough and agonizing, difficult and unappealing: tough neighborhood, tough exam, tough journey. They are not friendly; they do not suggest joy; they are in fact undesirable.

This is not so in the application of "tough" to a workout or to the performer of such a workout. Tough is not grim. Tough is very good, very cool, the embodiment of all that is strong and gutsy and exceptional. Tough is enviable and is to be embraced. A tough lifter faces a tough workout with a welcome chill, his head up and an unconscious correction of posture — it just happens.

Tough is tough, a badge of honor. Anyone who grumbles about tough, is not. Remember that, bombers. Tough is reserved for the silent fighter.

Got a Sec? Have a Question.

How are you?

How's the attitude, your mental acuity and focus, your general health and fitness level and your spiritual life? You feeling positive, hopeful and content? What about money, your income and financial security? Your job situation or career, is that area of your life promising, aspiring? And relationships — family and friends, your spouse, your sweetheart — are they contributing to your happiness and wholeness? Is there an evenness and balance in your emotions and an understanding of them to serve you well? Do you have good thoughts and a constructive imagination; are you uplifting among people, offering encouragement and affirmation? Are you optimistic should you find your mind drifting to thoughts of the future?

Is the stress of life under which we all function within control? Do you relax, laugh out loud; do you love?

How are your workouts going?

How's your strength, your energy and endurance? Is your training in good order? Do you have a solid plan with legitimate goals and a routine by which to achieve them? Is your training intensity sufficient, that is, are you blasting it? Are you applying common sense as you engage in your weight lifting, listening and feeling as your body guides you? Do you train with enthusiasm or a remnant of enthusiasm when the loving and driving force is in short supply? What level of concentration do you achieve as you seek a constructive workout, total or near total?

Besides your extreme focus, are your pace and groove and form near perfect or very good? As aches and pains and injuries visit you, do you submit beneath their rage or do you rise above them, mastering them, rather than being mastered by them, using them to learn and grow? Is consistency in your workouts held above all the variables that influence your muscular achievements? Do you allow negative imaginings to corrupt your training or is your mind clearly set on your goal? Do you apply supersets to saturate the muscles and develop cellular energy? Do you include heavy training regularly to build power and muscle mass and confront gravity with valor?

As you train day after day, are you gaining an understanding of your body in relation to different approaches and systems of training and not merely imitating programs suggested by trainers or magazines or dumb newsletters? Have you discovered inspiration for your workouts within yourself and the purpose you have, the motives that compel you and the goals that you clearly envision? Does desire — a heart for training — swell inside you regularly like a child's love for a puppy? Do you with unrelenting endurance seek the burn within the muscle during hard training? The pain and sacrifice associated with weight lifting, do you avoid the dubious duo or embrace them? Do you place the satisfaction of well-pumped muscles, the training afterglow, the taming of stress, the arousal of endorphins at the top of the list of life's favorite offerings? Are you discovering the control and command of musclebuilding, the expression of weight training and are you reaping at least a fistful of discipline and perseverance and patience?

How's your eating plan?

Have you been getting plenty of protein? Do you stay far away from the sugars and do you eat smaller meals more often throughout the day? I'm sure you're getting adequate fueling and nutritional support prior to your workout and shortly afterward for fortification and muscle repair, aren't you? And you know that a superior-quality whey-and-casein protein drink serves you effectively in providing added musclebuilding protein and nutrients throughout the day, especially around training sessions, don't you? Have you been taking your daily dosage of vitamins and minerals and antioxidants to assure your proper intake of those ingredients needed for the healthy functioning of your entire system? You know your intake of copious water is vital to your energy, cellular health and growth, detoxification, moment-to-moment function and long life, and your daily consumption is high and consistent, isn't it? Am I correct, of course, in assuming you don't smoke at all or drink in any way approaching excess? Allow me to be silly, but do you eat fast food and junk food or lint from your pockets? You don't eat too much, do you? You don't eat too little, do you? You don't go on binges or forget to eat for days, do you?

Just thought I'd ask.

Don't forget to wash behind your ears, brush your teeth and be good to your neighbor. Needless to say, feed your puppy.

Fuel's getting low. I'm taking her in and putting 'er to bed.

Consider how far you've come and imagine — visualize with certainty — where you want to go. The only thing that stands in your way is time and doubt. Time will pass, but doubt must be removed.

What you need to correct or alter in menu or exercise arrangement, attitude or workout intensity, you will surely attend along the way. Today's questions are tomorrow's answers. Trials, mistakes and injuries are the instructors.

Be strong, keep your sense of humor, stay alert, be positive and hopeful, drink your protein shakes, be nice to your neighbor, squat, of course, and don't ruin your shoulders with heavy bench pressing.

As far as it is possible, allow no unsightly gaps to develop in your eating scheme or your training thrust; they have a way of growing out of control and they are unbearable. Beware.

That we are aware of what we must do places us well above the rest. That we practice what we must puts us on top.

When in Doubt, Ramble On

I live in a small town on the coast of California, seventy-five miles south of San Francisco. The gym I train in is located in Santa Cruz, a town popular for its tourism, surfing and idyllic environment. One major coastal road, Highway 1, carries the travelers, commuters and locals, this way and that and over the past decade has become increasingly crowded. Sound familiar? The neighborhoods are stuffed, though a no-growth policy clutches the edges of the small governments concerned. Absolute gridlock between 3 and 7 PM has tortured the residents in recent years, more than a few pulling up stakes and heading to points north, south and east, where open space has yet to become shopping malls.

I've noticed a curious change of activity in the past six months. Not only is there less traffic on the gym floor, but also we can zoom home at 6 PM just like the good old days. One gets the strange feeling that the planet is being deserted, a creepy Twilight Zone hush whispers in one's ear.

What's up? Where'd everybody go? The population is growing on all continents and we know darn well we're not turning them back at the borders. Is everyone hiding out, less busy with work, less motivated and energized to play outdoors, poor or pennywise, strung out on TV, videos and Pizza Hut home delivery? Could it be economic confidence or the lack thereof, corporate thieves deep in our pockets, bad guys with bombs who hate us lurking in the dark, disputes on national fronts between swollen egos and a world growing smaller where the lives of oppressed people under cruel rule make us sad and anxious? Nah. How about Hollywood and television and violence glorified; something there might be distorting the enrapt minds of the rather large viewing audience, ya think? The experts say no. Acceleration of daily living, dilution of home and family, magnification of trivial differences, elaboration and validation of political correctness — do they have root in the curious local decrease of man and vehicles on the go in my neighborhood?

I can get used to this: more time, less aggravation, easier and simpler. I get to the gym quicker, when I choose, and not determined by traffic flow. I return home sooner and less stressed by the bumper-to-bumper boredom and battles.

Once at the gym I can dig into the job at hand with more energy and a clearer mind — my popular workout, which secretly supersedes all other occupations. And some days, like you, I need every bit of clarity and energy I can muster, every retreivable speck of purpose and inspiration that fell in the cracks and every loose thread of hope rewoven. Days without bright attention and optimism go by as if shunned or lost or buried. This is wrong. I must do my best always or suffer. You're nodding your head. Either you agree or you're falling asleep, who can tell?

Suffering (there are those among us who love misery and treat it as a diversion) often takes the form of hiccups, eye tics, spasms, shuddering, twitching and gas. On a bad day I'll have all six and squatting can be a nightmare. By the fifth rep I've lost count and can be halfway across the gym floor, a revolting predicament, but the show must go on.

I see a list forming.

- The show must go on.

- We must always do our best.

- We must rally clarity of mind, energy, purpose, inspiration, hope, optimism, enthusiasm and bright attention.

The right foods are important and the right routine is significant. These can be devised with common sense and resourcefulness and written in your log. There they are in black and white for your review and application. Review, the simple, clearly written reminder, arights our mental posture and engenders attention, order, direction and focus. The application, however, comes in a rainbow of colors from pale yellow through pink-orange to fire 'n' blood red, and in hot, warm and cold shades based on attitude and emotions, mental and physical well-being — well, what do you know, the list above. It's important to be in conscious tune with these variables regularly, thus providing the opportunity to dial them in, a preparation for your dynamic equalizer, the workout. It's part of the psyching process we go through as we approach any occasion of consequence.

I hear someone muttering in the bleachers that I'm a mental case and should be ignored. I'd add that was I not adhering to the above precepts I'd be a mental case that should be restrained. I'm not alone. Some of the healthiest people I know agree with my insanity.

So what's your point, Bomber? Okay. It's not in the dance; it's in the dancer. It's not in the act; it's in the actor. It's not in the bomb; it's in the bomber. I don't expect everyone to be ripping-nuts about their training — certainly some of us would be better off if we were not so wrapped up or enslaved, but positioning and casting a spotlight on the deed while it's onstage is our job, our role, our charge.

Doug entered the gym and walked past the juice bar where the famous Bomber shakes are blended and exciting discussions about building brawn take place. He looked up, nodded and plodded on toward the lockerroom. "Hey, Sparkle Plenty, what's new?" I asked, suspecting he could use a friend. Passing the test, he retraced his steps and leaned on the counter like a sack of wet sand.

"You feel okay, you got the bug, herpes?" I asked.

"No. Just one of those days," he said.

"Nothin's injured, you're not overdoing it?" I asked, probing further as if I was the doctor on duty.

"Nope."

"How's your fuel supply? Have you exhausted yourself on the job? Have you been getting adequate sleep, nourishment, protein? Any unordinary stress, feeling sorry for yourself, unfulfilled, how's your relationship with your girl? Am I going too far here? No, I'm not writing a book," I said, "Who'd read it?"

I didn't have a thermometer so his temp remained a mystery. I thought twice about taking his pulse (Doug had that "do not touch" look, if you know what I mean), but his forehead was dry, his eyes clear and his responses, though unexciting, were lucid. Stooped shoulders indicated a heavy unseen burden. This boy needs an attitude adjustment, I thought.

He'd dumped his hope in yesterday's garbage, un-renewed and unattended. His optimism was under a pile of dishes in the sink, sticky and gathering flies. Peak performance was in the laundry with his dirty underwear and socks.

He needed a transfusion of good thoughts to replace the negatives that had penetrated the thin skin of his unconscious mind. A fresh supply of encouragement would act as a natural stimulant and redirect his energy to a forward motion rather than draining his fuel stores in useless back-stepping. He's a good and generous man who works hard and it shows in his daily walk and talk and structure. He's simply forgotten and needs to be reminded, as we all do.

Because life seems to repeat itself — a total lie —we become bored and disregard the newness of each moment. Doug had submitted and his creative fluids ceased to flow. He had stalled. With no air under his wings, the bomber was in freefall. A jumpstart was needed. Training enthusiasm had to be regenerated by a massaging of the imagination and the suggestion of sure muscular growth and power advances.

I needed to act now while he was pliable and conscious. Condescension must not be detected and sincerity must rule. Easy.

"The main thing is you're here. It takes hidden courage to make it to the gym when you feellin' lousy. Most guys don't, they take the easy way out. I find I have the best workouts when I least expect it. I just don't push it, I don't do what I don't want to do, I don't expect too much and I'm plain thankful I'm on the floor pushing the iron. And then something happens and it all comes together. The blues fade and the weights start to move. Never fails."

Stiffness left his body and his face softened. Someone cared. Any other guy might be standing at a bar, twirling a shot glass with idle fingers and staring at an empty bowl of peanuts. What I said in a string of one-liners was more accurate than I first thought.

I leaned against the countertop and expertly polished glasses with a soft rag. Joe, the bartender. Order, the primary stabilizer, was quickly gained by pausing to restate his goals, list his menu and review his workout scheme. Where doubt was raised or discontent evident, we sorted and smoothed things out with basic touches. Hate hanging leg-raises and press-behind-necks? Get rid of them and do rope tucks and seated front presses instead. Keep it happy. Hate tuna and water? Dump them and eat sardines and goat's milk instead. Smile. Small joke from the Bomber, though it might carry some real credibility.

Pour me another one, Joe.

I asked Doug if he'd thought about standing curls and how they recruit a vast complex of muscles providing muscular benefits and body power beyond the biceps' simple activity only. We talked about smart ways to combine exercises with pace to affect a momentum and spirit in training that captures our attention and promotes harder work and greater muscle response and maximum fulfillment. I revived the subjects of stress reduction, hormonal stimulation and balance and the joys of power in the grip and health in the bones and the absolute thrill of not being a turnip.

Doug was sitting upright on the swivel stool sipping a Jucy Lucy, his favorite Bomber special. His voice had gained muscularity and his eyes, intensity. He said, as if reading cue cards from the rejected *Brother Iron* screenplay, "This isn't something we must do to live a long and strong life only; we lift weights because we love it and because it's a sure way to express ourselves positively in a world where too many pretend, imitate, lie and waste."

He gripped the styrofoam cup and I thought it was gonna burst — Jucy Lucy all over the ceiling.

"The only way to train is to blast it," he said.

I've created a monster.

Weight lifting is good for the heart and soul, does wonders for the body and makes us strong. It's fun and fulfilling and adds wonderful years to our life. Why, then, doesn't everyone lift weights?

Some see the mountain, some climb the mountain, and some find the mountain in the way. They ask why the mountain is there and how to go around it. For some, the mountain does not exist.

Bring on the Pool, Hot Tub and Dancing Girls

How many times have you said, no way do I want to be as big as Ronnie Coleman? Yeah, me neither. What would we do with all that extra, weird muscle? A nuisance, really. I just want to be half as big. This I can work into my schedule... it's more realistic and not so freaky. Right!

A couple came into the gym not so long ago looking like a pair of middle-aged porcupine in a field of wolves. I stood close enough to say, "How are you?" but not so close as to get a quill in my sweats. After I assured them that I wasn't there to sell them a membership, rob or mock them, they relaxed and pointed out that they weren't interested in building massive muscular bodies. Oh, really!

"We simply want to get in shape for the summer and our twentieth high school reunion in July."

He eyed the menu hanging above the juice bar and ordered a Jucy Lucy with extra Mango extract. She fussed with her pantsuit that was beginning to gather around her thighs, "Where's the pool and hot tub?"

I stood my ground and contemplated the typical and sad catastrophe before me. No pool or hot tub to be found, I suggested they consider a more aggressive approach to getting in shape by applying sensible weight training and sensible eating for the next month or the rest of their lives. Her name was Millie and I think she actually hissed under her breath. Biff was content scanning the gym floor and slurping his hefty protein drink in disguise. He thought out loud that maybe the weights were the way to go. "We could hire a personal trainer for a few weeks and learn the ropes, Dear." She frowned and took a gulp of his drink, then another and another. She drained the 24-ounce foam cup and tossed it.

The gym has a selection of aerobic equipment neatly laid out on an L-shaped balcony with plenty of height, light, viewpoint, breeze and TVs. This pressed Millie's button (moving treadmills, climbers and such with computer boards... civilization), and Biff got an appointment with a trainer the following morning. They both were relieved with a trial pass, giving them a chance to try out the ole shoe to see if it fit.

"There's something you need to know," I called out as they headed for the door of escape. They thought they were free, but I grabbed them by the seats of their pants. Looking directly into their eyes, I said, "What you are casually undertaking this day is probably the most significant responsibility of your lives: your physical health and welfare. Most folks grow up and grow older and watch from a safe distance. Today you've decided to participate. You're going to love this. Get a good night's sleep."

They showed up early — their day off —revealing a humility and reserve undetectable the day before. New sweats, gym bags, sneakers and water bottles — matching bookends ready for a marathon. They headed for the bikes without preamble. A ten-minute warm-up before mild crunches and leg raises was the order of the day. In five minutes the sense of involvement was achieved and they began to feel loose, sweaty and comfortable.

It turns out he had recently been diagnosed with adult onset diabetes and she had been... er... sort of binge eating regularly. Married for a bunch of years, their small thriving business is in the convulsing industry of computer engineering. Stress had a strangle hold on them. They were overweight, under-muscled, weak and vulnerable. They were brilliant, yet ignorant. I think they were lonely. They were riding the bikes, smiling and I was filling them with propaganda. The Goodwill Conspiracy.

Crunches and leg raises on floor mats were less of a delight, but they endured like champs. They hit the gym floor and were guided to the Hammer Chest Press for shoulders, chest and tris, mixed with the seated lat pull for back and bis — enough for one day. Three sets of 12 reps, pushing and pulling alternately and they were pumped and pooped. As they cooled off, unwound and delighted in their achievement, we walked the gym floor and I demonstrated the equipment. It was their first workout in a tired and mishandled lifetime. The workout was over and a renewed lifetime had just begun.

Here's to commitment, discipline, courage and fear. They come in four to six days a week around sunrise to get a giant step on the lovable old anxious world and spend some exhilarating time with new, like-minded friends. Millie eats the right foods in the right amounts (usually good nutrition accompanies good training) and I'm almost embarrassed when she pulls on the seat of her swestpants to show me how much weight she's lost. Biff no longer takes medication and all the symptoms of diabetes are gone. They are really good people and no one really knew it, Millie and Biff included.

A true story. Only the names, places and circumstances have been changed to protect the innocent. This is the Bomber signing off. May your squats always go up and your bench press never go down.

Torn Quads and Growing Waistlines Unite

Early last winter I engaged in a fiery squat workout that overloaded my legs for a week. A good time to rest and repair, right? Well, in four days I was again up for my regular lower body routine and thought I'd toss a few sets of light squats around to stimulate the tired muscles, maintain my schedule and feed the neurosis. Third set, fifth rep something gurgled and rippled deep in the right quad. I looked in the mirror through slitted eyes and asked myself a plausible question, "So, Wonder Boy, do you put the bar back where it belongs or are you going to do another rep to see if the thigh is really injured?" I don't know what possessed me at that moment, but I reluctantly racked the nasty thing and pouted.

I nursed the self-diagnosed muscle tear with time and conservative thigh training. Partial leg presses of the light-weight, high rep variety, cautious leg extensions, curls and calves half-heartedly comprised my lower body agenda. Occasionally, I sneaked under the Top Squat for sets of 95 and 135 to check out the action, knowing that small tears become large tears with very little persuasion. A very touchy injury with no sense of humor greeted me predictably every time and a month ago I shrugged my shoulders and accepted that time and gravity are nuisances with which one must reckon wisely and courageously — the dirty rats. Why add frustration and hazard to the abominable list of limiting factors? Growl, hiss.

Without squats I was a dog without his bark and no tail to wag; I lost my doggedness. Slow and deliberate leg presses with a pause at the bottom, going deeper with successive workouts, gave a shadow of pleasure to my leg training and I settled for the compromise. I missed two, three or four plates on each side of the bar, the tight reps, the exhilaration and the famous over-all body demand. What the heck.

After returning from a short vacation I resumed my workouts with patient ease, allowing myself to enjoy the reviving movements, the cool pace and calculated form. Slow-rep warm-ups are very important in preparing the muscles and joints and insertions for hard work and are a valid representation of the training output, I observed. They count. There was a time when I regarded warming up with scorn: What a waste. Now they are absolutely necessary; they enable. A curious thought crossed my mind: Early last winter in an approach to shorten my leg program, conserve energy (an overtraining consideration) and eliminate pre-exhausting the quadriceps, I discontinued the decade-long practice of tri-setting leg extensions with curls and calves prior to my squatting — just about the same time I endured the tear to the thigh. Coincidence?

The tear is on the mend. I re-installed the pre-squat, extension, curl, calf tri-set and today hung three-and-a-half plates on the bar for reps. How long will it be before I load four-and-a-half plates or return to the leg press, only time and gravity can tell. Until further notice, I'm mean, barking and wagging my tail.

Might I trust that I have satisfactorily warmed you up, so to speak, and gained your confidence? Only with you fully on my side may I confront the tough topic before us.

We've spoken candidly about the superior condition of the universal waistline, it's largeness and roundness. More than big, the subject is serious and delicate and, therefore, difficult to approach. How do I speak of man and woman's fatness without hurting, angering or demeaning the beholder while none of those griefs are intended?

I pause, write, delete and pause again. I dare not mock, judge or patronize, yet the message I choose to relate is hard and must be driven home hard. What good is it if the facts and figures are offered with soothing kindness and the intended recipients are stroked and lulled and treated as if it's a common dilemma we should one day address? Girth-enhanced friends, let's give reduction our best shot, perhaps, with a little... um, exercise and diet... sorry, just kidding... what came over me? Over-weightedness and tummy-challenged is as kind as I can get and it's ruinous. Again, I halt, think, write and delete. My thoughts don't reach the page; I have no right to be so harsh. I'm a regular fathead.

I observed those around me as I meandered across the states on a recent get-away. I saw obesity with every focus of the eye. Wherever I looked, there it was; chubby, chunky, plump, big-bellied, great-bellied, pot-bellied, beer-bellied, over-stuffed: men, moms, cute girls, babies, boys too round to run — trying to sit, trying to stand, working hard getting in and out of their car, hiking to the restroom or playing in the park.

In ten days I encountered one tall bodybuilder from the Twin Cities Gym, one eighteen-year-old stud from Gold's in Utah and three possibles from who knows where; they spoke in a language full of guttural sounds. Jersey, maybe, or Romania. Yes, I realize this is a cursory cross-section and not representative of the states or the globe, and it gets better in some regions and worse in others. But I suspect my overall observations are reasonably accurate. Fatness and its attendant limitations rule big time.

Interestingly, this is not striking news. We all know about the existing circumstances. The media throws out some bones about obesity, exercise and diet, just enough to dilute the message, tame the beast, satisfy public health and safety announcements, serve the political machine or make big bucks on the casualty.

But no one (far too few to mention... you and I, perhaps) is alarmed, frightened or ashamed enough to act with deliberation, commitment and intelligence... with guts. Do we huddle together semi-passively, now the slim minority, and pretend to agree that carrying some extra pounds can't be all that bad? After all, everyone else does, it's sort of normal. Are we fixed in place; do we deny and ignore? Does misery truly love company? What else are we: oblivious, hopeless, apathetic, lethargic, lazy, ignorant and complacent?

Bold and informed individuals stand up and with compassionate urgency and accuracy answer questions and offer solutions regarding the evergrowing predicament of evergrowing. The huffing masses look tentatively at one another with dull eyes and slide lower in their recliners.

I applaud those who work extensively against the odds with hormonal and genetic disadvantages, those whose battle is bitter and ongoing. You are the rare and devoted. God's speed. We've embarked on a long and formidable journey out of control at every turn. Where control is in your hands, don't let go.

No problem for bombers.

When in doubt, take it to the gym. The answer has a way of surfacing and the doubt has a way of disappearing somewhere between the barbells and dumbbells. I've never encountered a problem that didn't grow smaller after ten minutes in the gym and under the iron.

You Lift, You Learn, You Grow

We are, none of us, immune. Anyone at any time will doubt, wonder, become uncertain or subtly negative. A wary nature is insurance, an essential of survival and an internal mechanism directing us toward a good life. In excess, caution can paralyze us or, at least, render life and living a harmless and uneventful occurrence. Suspicious, ever-questioning and procrastinating souls with wrinkled-up noses capture doubt and uncertainty, stuff and mount it over the mantle to be safely displayed as trophies of conquests never made. The wall upon which our trophies, yours and mine, would hang is bare. We have no articles to show or emblems to share; no snarling beasts mounted for a viewer's pleasure or our conceit. We've wrestled them to the ground and left them for dead.

I think back, long and hard. At twelve I didn't ask what I should do. Who could I ask? What would I ask? I just did it. At seventeen I didn't ask what exercise builds this and what food builds that. Thank God, I just did it, more and harder. I don't ever remember asking much; never seemed that complicated. No one had to tell me it was hard work and took a long time. School was hard work and took a long time. Working after school to earn a few bucks was hard and took time. Why should lifting weights and building muscle be any different? You lift, you learn, you grow. That's life.

Today? Not so simple. How could it be and why should it be? The curve is different: more acute and active and occupied. Questions are no longer questions but riddles to be cleverly circulated. The absence of quickness and efficiency in a solution reduces it to a lie. Let's do it now, let's do it right, let's do it perfectly (pssst... cheating is okay) and at once — before the other guy (everyone else is the other guy). That's the message I've been hearing lately.

You can always tell when somebody's been watching too much TV, CNN and infomercials.

Building a strong and healthy body need not be sought that way (zoom, zoom), nor can it be achieved that way. In fact, it's a contradiction, isn't it? A hurried and anxious method of operation produces only injury, disappointment and stress, not the soundness of body, the fulfillment of accomplishment and the relief of tension that ought to be associated with hardy fitness.

Let's say you know all this. You've been around a few years and to be called well seasoned is as good as compliments get. Time is square enough, a peculiar, almost lovable mate you've come to know and can't deny. Success and disappointment in their own relative ways have come to visit, linger and leave.

You're a mature bodybuilder and the scenery appears to be changing. You still love to train, meet goals and reinvent yourself, but call it age or possibly just a slump, you now seem to be faced with questions that only a wiser bodybuilder can answer.

Things like: Am I training hard enough or overtraining? If I push myself to do one or two more reps, is that good or am I over doing it? Sometimes I go to the gym and can train like a horse, strong and energetic. Sometimes I battle with, "Should I rest today or push myself? Why does my elbow joint hurt? Am I getting arthritis? What is the most effective way for me to train?" I used to do cardio exercise every day to help with bodyfat loss, energy increase and heart health. Am I overdoing it? It now seems to cut into my training energy where it never did before. I'm out of control.

The last paragraph includes a list of questions recently offered by an established bodybuilder approaching the broadening span of middle age; he's intelligent, realistic and persevering. His questions are legitimate and I ask them myself, frequently. I'm one of those coonskin-capped pioneers with a Bowie knife fixed in his teeth, clawing to broaden the great span and push aging over the edge. Exhausting, but I've got an enthusiastic audience cheering me on. I continue to address these vivid issues in my typical "this is what I'd do if I were you" style.

Of course, I first need to take my afternoon snooze and my medications and soak my feet and apply ice to my left shoulder, heat to my right shoulder. Or is it the other way around?

You ever stop and think about your workouts and note the positive effect they have on the rest of your life and those around you? Not the obvious benefits — energy, strength, improved appearance, attitude and vitality — but the distinguishing abstract qualities that position you high on the coveted list of neat, good and nice people.

Those sterling characteristics you possess are responsible for and have developed as a result of your pursuance of muscle and might, and positively affect your neighbor: discipline, motivation, courage, perseverance, patience, order and confidence. You're a team leader, can think fast and you never give up. You really are swell.

You Win, You Lose, You Crawl

Seldom do I drag myself to the gym unwillingly. It's not often I stand before the barbells and dumbbells with drooping shoulders and hesitation. And though I don't feel like Superman, never do I question why I'm about to fatigue myself and inflict hard work and pain upon my body for several hours. That's all behind me and has been for a long, long time. Today, I roll out the ole Harley, run a cloth over the chrome, crack the pipes and let 'er rip. I speak metaphorically. My Harley is gone, along with my twenty-inch arms.

This all began many years ago.

I remember when I was a kid; no problem, the weights were playthings. You push, pull, toss, lift and grunt. Great fun.

Clank, rattle; where's my wrench? As a teen, lifting was like a sport you played; you win, you lose, the days came and went and skipping a workout was no big deal. Let's see, should I lift weights or play stickball at the park?

One day — who remembers when; it's all a haze — I noticed guilt had taken up residence in my ever-present shadow, a nagging, smirking wise guy — a jerk, really — that made me irritable when I missed a workout, miserable if I was delinquent a week. Training became important, a thing I had to do, and the fun was leaking away. Most anything became more desirable than the weights; studying Latin, changing the oil in a Nash or cleaning the stinking garage. Thank heaven there was no TV. I pressed on.

Then some raggedy habit took form and the walk to the weight room became regular, and labored and cheerless. It's lonely on this bench, under this bar, counting these sets and reps. How many do I have to do today? Nine zillion? The number was a pain in my head and completing the prescribed task before me was a dull feat. 20 (ugh), 19 more (aay), 18 (oof), 17 (urp). "Will the workout ever end?" was my approach. The color around me was gray, the odor stinky and the taste had a subtle hint of metallic. Sensitive guy that I am, I faithfully pressed on.

It wasn't long before anticipation, the kind with a sour puss, started hanging around with guilt. Put these two thugs together and we have tension, nervous tension. Now it's not only hard work and lonely under the bar, it's tiresome and exhausting thinking about it, all day, at work, at lunch, on the road and in the sack. By the time I got to the gym, I'd been there, done that. Not another rep! I'm whooped! Push that iron.

Swell, but that's not enough. Besides feeling guilty for missing a workout I haven't missed and badgered by a workout I haven't hit, I'm feeling disappointed with the progress I haven't made. A mob is gathering in my shadow and I'm just a skinny kid. We have Guilty Gus, Big Al Anticipation and the notorious Duke of Disappointment conspiring in the dark. Step aside, ya mutts, I'm using that rack.

Duty calls when you're still and listen to your soul. Taking down the three over-stuffed conniving bums became my mission and I knew it; the first sign of instinct — survival of the fittest — which plays no minor role in the musclebuilder's life. Instinct rules.

In this life you win, you lose or you crawl. It's not that I wanted to win, but I refused to lose and I will not crawl.

Elementary, really, and I worked by elimination. I deduced from their focus upon me that that which I focused upon was worthy and right because they're so bad. In spite of or because of the combined efforts of the devious threesome, I pressed on.

I discovered devotion and intensity.

Strangely, my shadow grew larger with my body and the three wise guys grew smaller. In time I replaced guilt with discipline, a stern yet agreeable character. Negative anticipation submitted to positive preparation and psyching up, a pair of confident characters with lofty goals. And disappointment, sour and ungrateful, left one fine day without a whimper. Like mistakes, the scoundrels taught tough lessons. Their departure was an welcome relief, dirty snow and slippery ice melting in the spring.

The walk to the gym became hurried, not soon enough, and excitement accompanied my footsteps. Miles were behind me and miles were ahead and somehow I knew the way. You never know the way unless you walk it and climb it, get lost and lose ground, grow cold and hungry, and insist on walking some more. Nobody can tell you exactly the what, how and why of a thing, they can only offer wise suggestions and solid encouragement , gold ore and uncut diamonds.

S'cuz me, Bub. What's the big deal? It's only lifting weights — exercise and good food. It's not life, liberty and the pursuit of happiness. You got a point to make? The train is leaving the station; the bombers are taking to the air.

So now where am I — where are we — in my recollections? When did the pleasure of training settle in my bones? When I stepped back and realized its worth; when I resumed doing it for its adventure and immediate reward; when I trusted its permanence; when training was no longer an obligation, but a wise choice, a desirable means to eliminate barriers and overcome obstacles and to express myself without screaming for an hour or two, several times a week.

And it's no big ego trip to enjoy physical strength, endurance, reasonable confidence and a body that doesn't resemble a pear balanced precariously on two straws. No more ego than a long list of letters after one's name on a letterhead, a tattoo in the right place, a red Carrera in the driveway, a thousand-dollar suit or a shaved head. It took some time, pressed together with considerable doubt, curiosity, pain and sacrifice to make the discovery, but it's worth it. To settle into your training with confidence is like sitting back in an easy chair listening to music. Comfortable and relaxed. Just don't fall asleep on me, bombers, we have work to do — clearing the runway, fueling up, checking the landing gear and adjusting the struts.

Of course, the choir agrees and loves to be reminded. How about you, whose t-shirts are getting snug and triceps are forming horseshoes?

Those who are relatively new yet proudly invested and struggle to maintain their training balance, focus and zeal can reduce the less-than-delightful learning and growing curve by accepting today the precepts put forth on these pages. A mouthful; read that again, slowly and out loud. Trust, press on toward your admirable goal and invest your time with renewed enthusiasm, because it's happening and happens no other way.

Consider how far you've come and imagine — visualize with certainty — where you want to go. The only thing that stands in your way is time and doubt. Time will pass, but doubt must be removed. What you need to correct or alter in menu or exercise arrangement, attitude or workout intensity, you will surely attend along the way. Today's questions are tomorrow's answers. Mistakes and injuries and practice are the instructors.

Be strong, keep your sense of humor, stay alert, be positive and hopeful, drink your protein shakes, be nice to your neighbor, squat, of course, and don't ruin your shoulders with heavy bench pressing. As far as it is possible, allow no unsightly gaps to develop in your eating scheme or your training thrust; they have a way of growing out of control and they are unbearable. Beware.

That we are aware of what we must do places us well above the rest. That we practice what we must puts us on top.

Let's taxi down the runway, bombers, and take off one by one in fine formation till we fill the skies with roaring and fill our hearts with inspiration.

Go. You first, I'll follow.

Intensity defines one's achievement.

Intensity is a state of training performance. Seek it, locate and define it; research and study it as you apply it, determine the measure that is personally agreeable, desirable and lock on. This is your target intensity as you focus on your workouts, your level of exercise output based on pressure and pain and your willingness to endure it. Embrace it and know it, understand it. It has the personality of a dear and dependable friend.

Thorns and Roses

There's nothing like a vigorous workout to blunt the sting of a thorny day. Thorns are interesting devices of nature, nasty in construction, yet existing in the environment to protect and preserve. I bear a few thorns myself and suspect I am not alone.

We need to be sharp in the increasingly dangerous and cynical world we live in and the barbs we encounter are unfailing reminders. Look sharp, stay sharp and watch your back sounds obsessive, but it's not the worst counsel one can give. This caution requires awareness and self-preservation, discipline and hard work. The trick is not to become a prickly thorn in the process.

Again, I return to my workouts to strengthen me against the sharp spines that claw at my flesh. Training has a way of making me bigger and stronger, while reducing me in size at the same time. Such is the paradox that provides both shield and armament, enabling me to trek through the day without backing down or striking a blow.

Barbs can be spiky formations of our own making. One of our most piercing shortcomings is our lack of gratefulness for things small and commonplace. We take life for granted; we hurry to gain more or we idly sit and watch the world go by. Life's grand, but we fail to notice. The bad, though outweighed by its opposite, is sought after and magnified, sometimes glorified. We allow, almost encourage, it to grow, like a devilish, hypnotic wildfire. We should extinguish the spitting and fitful flames, but their searing intensity penetrates our soul like Lady Luck.

A workout in down times is akin to a life preserver to a drowning man. I know men and women who deteriorate when their day-to-day training routine is disrupted. It's a swarm embrace to the brokenhearted, a consolation to the overwhelmed, a friendly place to the lost and lonely, freedom to the trapped, a solid expression for the voiceless and an elixir to the weak and downtrodden. Workouts can breathe life into a hopeless form.

Lest we forget, health and fitness through lifting and smart nutrition is a passionate lifestyle for a select culture of bright people. They are few, but they are strong. They find delight in training, as they balance and temper their lives. Sharing disciplines, sacrifices, grunts and groans, a distinct joy is evident among those dedicated to the cast-iron cause. And a dust of rust adds fine flavor, color and credence to the deed.

Believe it or not, people have been restored to life by the energy gained from a good workout. I once knew a man who knew a man who was critically ill, and the worst was expected. One sad afternoon the fellow was pronounced clinically dead.

An alert team of personal trainers hooked him to a defibrillator charged by electricity generated by twenty-five stationary bikes powered by robust athletes from the neighborhood gym. He was revived instantly.

A true story, they say. Why would I lie to you?

Working out adds sensitivity and awareness to the heart and mind of the dedicated lifter. Beware, you say: The softer side of life with its fine qualities can be pierced by daily thorns and render them harmless. You can be sure of this: The sensitivities gained by lifting weights are about as soft as the iron that formed them. Thorns are made dull and pointless when forced to penetrate the backside of seasoned lifters. Rather, they are gathered into a heap and used as fuel to increase the heat of a workout. Hot thorns!

My life, I admit, is a prickly mess when my workouts are not in order. Further, it's difficult to determine which came first, the prickly mess or the workout disorder. You can bet I've spent many fruitless afternoons trying to sort out this conundrum, only to slip into the gym out of frustration, have a monster workout and forget whatever it was that puzzled me — further support that a good workout removes the prick from prickly, the stick from stickers and the barb from nasty barbules. The point? Pointy objects beware.

I think we're getting somewhere.

Don't you love it when your training is in good order; you're regularly arriving at the gym on time, you're unhurried and you know what you want, can and should do, and the latter three needs are in harmony? The energy is solid, the pump is within reach, the equipment is available and you're in good repair. Life's not perfect and you accept its flaws.

The weights feel tight and your muscles feel hard and the joints feel loose and the groove is smooth and easy. You settle in, you flow., you become absorbed — distractions are locked out, focus locked in. The first sixty minutes go by firmly and you're in charge, the next fifteen minutes are a good fight and the last fifteen are a winning struggle to the end... you walk away without a limp.

The thorns drop like dried leaves in the fall. They no longer scratch, draw blood or impart pain. They disintegrate, they evaporate, they dissolve. They are no more.

In my fight against stress, doubt, fear, anger and insecurity, no weapon or defense serves me more effectively than a strong bout with the iron. One might suggest confronting the source of the conditions directly, but their origins are often disguised, hidden or unapproachable. Through the force exerted during a good workout, and the discipline and focus to apply such a force, troubles are clarified, diminished, resolved or eliminated.

And this not by magic.

It has something to do with — I'm guessing as usual — the release of endorphins in the brain that soothe our pain and induce euphoria. There is the distraction of exercise that frees our subconscious to work on problems unimpeded by our oft-confused conscious minds. There's the fulfillment of concrete achievement in our daily life, augmenting our confidence and undermining our doubt and insecurity. Further, we can't deny the real and concrete physical power, energy and well-being — exhilaration — we derive from the mighty expression. That mighty armor and weaponry will conquer the foe.

And then there is exactly that: the expression we make by hefting heavy metal over our heads, clearly conveying who we are, at once a declaration, admission, confession and revelation. Such is the need and tendency of the individual aware of his individuality, to speak out through his action and deeds.

Let's not dwell on the brier patch. Take one nettle at a time and allow it to direct your course. We learn from our mistakes, stumbles and stings. The point is this: Be aware and beware of thistle and thorn, be prepared for them, heed them, walk a circle around them, nip them in the bud, dull their edges and when you must, set them ablaze. Don't let their sharp points penetrate your tender yet toughened skin.

As weight lifting goes a long way to tear down our enemies and portray who we are, so does the moving of iron develop our flesh and bones, our heart and lungs. Only a whack or a liar would claim he doesn't want strong muscles and well-formed body. Muscles are cool and might is in.

When the sun is warm and overhead and the roses are flourishing and standing tall and my heart is filled with goodness, yet it's time to clear the thriving patch of brier, this is what I do: I say to heck with the dagger-sharp thorns, I'm coming through. Got my gym bag and rosin and wraps and belt and favorite t-shirt; got my water bottle and protein shake; got my thick bars and handles and gym floor strewn with steel.

I've got a beating heart and a handful of exercises, from presses to curls and deadlifts to squats. I know a rep from a set and I can count to twenty if I have to. I've the got time; I've got the will; I've got the guts; I've got the love.

The sun never sets on those who fly high, long and swiftly toward its brilliant and life-giving rays. Stay warm, stay cool.

Steady as she goes, bombers...

Dave

Afterword
Behind the Smile

Muscle and Fitness, a colorful and energetic riot of musclemen and musclebuilding information, isn't a recent publication that gained popularity overnight. It has gone by a variety of names over half a century and was reared by a guy named Joe Weider. Joe, dubbed the Trainer of Champions, dragged it from the ink-smeared pages of a manual printing press in his grandma's Montreal apartment and gave it dramatic life based upon his vision of muscle and might.

I was one of the characters who played a role in his elaborate vision, a Mr. America and Mr. Universe in the dream he presented to the world. Appearing on the scene in the early '60s, I filled the pages of his magazines, adorned their covers and, through inspiring pictures on California beaches, conveyed stories of delight, promise and hope to the young and young at heart.

I smiled broadly, flexed my muscles and frolicked with beach bunnies on lazy, crazy sunny afternoons. The blue Pacific rolled in mightily, billowy clouds with silver linings caressed the horizons and dogs playfully chased seagulls along endless sandy shores. Hop in. The water's fine. Life is grand.

Hold it there. Back up twenty feet and take another look. I see a distressed cameraman and his elaborate gear in a heap of cases, containers and bags; I see a guy — that must be Joe — in half a suit with his sleeves and trouser legs rolled up; off to the side a group of sticky, uninterested bystanders mope about, kick sand and suck on water bottles. These must be the delighted characters in the delightful pictures awaiting a moment of delight.

The sun pours down, hot and relentless, and more baby oil is applied to the muscular bodies. A pump is sought to give vibrancy to fatigued and dehydrated muscles; instead itchy sand is distributed generously to far reaches of the body — ears, eyes, nose and every known crack and crevice. Are we having fun yet?

Now the sun is going down and neither the cameraman nor the subjects can delay the untimely process. Joe is flailing his arms, while Artie Zeller or Russ Warner or Jimmy Caruso — bless their hearts — tries hopelessly to interpret his wild gesticulations. Reflectors are brought in, the location is moved, the ocean grows calm and the dramatic lighting is lost to soft shadows suitable for capturing romance, a bottle of wine and thou. Not good.

But wait! The sun's lowering rays join their own reflection off the ocean's surface and the bodies amid the stunning light are spectacular. Everyone is by some freak of nature in the right spot at the right time and in the right mood. Joe screams at Artie, whose nose is deep in his film bag, to take the picture now, now, now.

Art Zeller is a master photographer and physiques are his specialty. He knows what to do, when and how. The digital camera is not even a dream of the future and, alas, our patient and sensible lensman fusses with his ole' reliable Roloflex. Joe is now tearing at his shirt and performing what appears to be an Indian rain dance and whooping, "Artie, Artie! Shoot the picture! Shoot the picture!" Without hesitation Artie shouts, "Joe, the camera is out of film." Joe, with a child's authority and desperation shrieks, "Shoot it anyway!"

Artie did. Joe was pleased. Another day at the beach.

The pretty models went their way — they could care less for muscleheads in the 1960s — and the muscleheads went theirs. The first thing on their minds was protein and then a workout missed due to the fun and frolic at the beach. But it was worth it, wasn't it? Maybe your mug will be in the mag and you'll be famous. In those days fame and glory in a muscle magazine and ten cents got you a cup of coffee.

Hey, buddy, can ya spare a dime?

Undeniably, the most inspiring and pleasant photographic sessions were experienced during the winter. Not! Though snow does not fall, nor the temperatures drop below 50 in southern California, winter is winter is winter. Tis the season for hibernation, losing the tan and gaining weight to accommodate heavy off-season training. Repair and grow, relax and attend life beyond cuts and striations is the bodybuilder's theme. Let's go to the mountains, the deserts or visit the folks back east. Throw in a few year-end holidays and you've got bulky, round and white all over.

"What's that you say? Pictures on the beach this Saturday? What beach? I thought the beach dried up in the winter, was evacuated, dismantled or closed for repairs."

"An up-coming summer promotion needs to be shot now, Bomber, or I'm out millions of bucks."

Oh! In that case, don't want to lose my eighty-five-dollar-a-week shipping clerk's salary. Sure, JW, see ya there... bright and early... I'll bring coffee. The grazing white rhinoceros in Dave Draper's trunks will be me.

I'm training hard, strong as a hippo and about as shapely. Put me on a beach and big-game hunters from miles around will gather to claim me as a trophy. You can't do this, Joe. I'm too young to die. Not the beach. Flash! Cover boy is as white as a blank billboard and twice as big. The only definition I have goes something like this: bulky, rounded, colorless, foolish, unwilling, miserable, pouty.

Breaking News: Unidentified Blimp Hovers Aimlessly Over Southern California Beaches. No Details at This Time.

Smiles form with difficulty on frigid lips. The air is cold and nippy breezes supply shivers in spasms. The unlikely crew of plump and pasty bodies huddles under beach towels to stay warm and protect themselves from blasts of sandy wind. The ocean is ominous, the beach is desolate and surviving seagulls are inland hiding under bushes. Dogs and their owners are home where it's safe and cozy. February is no time for these shenanigans. Neither is July for that matter.

Joe is quite a character and has more color than a rainbow and twice the gold found at the end. He loves the bodybuilding scene, gave it a stage upon which to play and did more to present it to the world than anyone.

Anyone, that is, except the players themselves. Praise be to musclemen who, driven by passion and desire, did what they did because they had to do it.

The smiles on the beaches were hard-earned and their payment was gained in the dark confines of gyms filled with heavy iron. Weights — barbells and dumbbells — were the source of resistance that built the muscles that built the men that built the magazine. I, and the guys before me, lifted the cold and noisy metal not for a moment on a page of paper, but for reasons — wonderful reasons — too numerous to count.

Oh, heck! Let me give it a try. I'll be brief.

There's health, muscle and might for starters. Not bad. There's the fun of lifting weights and the exciting challenge it presents, the physical pushing and pulling and stretching, the intelligent formation of exercises, movements and routines, and the tantalizing pumping, burning and striving. Weight training is a dynamic diversion providing strong camaraderie, identification and hope. Be sure of this: Few pastimes provide more benefits, rewards and fulfillment.

Training builds discipline, perseverance and patience. Mountains are climbed with these superior characteristics, lives are saved and nations are shaped. Tough exercise puts order and rhythm in our lives, diminishing confusion and reducing stress, and that's worth more than a few trips to the psychiatrist's couch. As quality is added to life, so is it extended with enduring, useful and enjoyable years. When once we said, "I can't," after gaining fitness and well-being through dedicated exercise, we say, "Don't just sit there, let's get moving."

A strong back and strong heart match one's courage and confidence, four natural byproducts of working out and regular lifting. And, though personally pleased, true ironheads don't brag about their accomplishments — one more modest attribute gained from solid cast-iron training.

I said I was gonna be brief.

Not all the fun was captured on the beaches of sunny California. There were the eight- and ten-story abandoned buildings in the old garment district of Manhattan. Somehow we gained admittance to these deteriorating fire hazards and were dragged by chattering and screeching cables of old industrial lifts to forsaken levels high above alleys and dumpsters below. After clearing a corner of over-turned benches, work-tables and indeterminable debris, we settled in to serious photography. A white backdrop was hung in contrast to the dust and mold, and spider webs as thick as tapestries in a haunted house. The rats kept to themselves; I was more concerned with the warped floorboards that shook perceptibly as we traversed our surroundings, soldiers in a minefield.

The camera sat on its tripod, the lights and reflectors and umbrellas were in place and the champion stood on his mark, all objects precisely determined by strings with signifying knots in measured placements. The oil is smoothly applied after a hint of a pump is gained by flexing in place. Swell! Move from your mark, you get smudged and grimy, splintered and wounded, infected and quarantined. The trouble starts when a thirsty star asks for a slug of water. It's hot and stuffy in New

York City in August. No water. It worsens when he has to go to the men's room. No plumbing.

No problem is too big or too small for a band of smiling bodybuilders.

"One, two, three and flex. Again, and this time, Dave, twist harder and don't forget to flex your legs. Jimmy, is he standing in the right spot? One, two, three and flex. That was good, Bomber. Once more, this is for a cover. Twist and bring your arms higher... flex your legs. NO, no, no! Caruso, you tell him! Twist, flex, arms higher, higher... Smile."

I'll tell you this: No one got the poses and the photographs like Joe Weider.

Once I stood in the center of Century Plaza, on the granite edge of a stunning water fountain. The size of a tennis court, the fountain adorned the center-divide of Century Boulevard and was framed by towering thirty-story glass-fronted office buildings to the east and west. Water gushed brilliantly toward the sky, and I nonchalantly busied myself while glowing with oil in my teal posing trunks waiting for Russ Warner to prepare his camera, position himself and position me. It was high noon — lunchtime, in the bustling, sophisticated business district of Beverly Hills, home of world finance and filmmaking. Traffic was heavy and animated. No problem, I'm cool. I've been stared at before.

"Yeah, you too, wise guy!!"

Oh, look. Russ is talking to some policemen who are pointing at me. Old friends, no doubt, but I refrain from waving. Rather than pump up, I try to look very small as I stroll through the slightly slimy shallow pool to the other side. Chilly. Halfway there I hear the whoop-whoop sound emergency vehicles make when they approach an intersection and want it cleared immediately. I return to my original post — dripping wet — and, as if responding to their signal, hit an overhead, double-arm biceps shot, a side back shot and a kneeling side chest. I'm

Mr. America, after all. I bow and wait for the traffic to subside before I jaywalk and join them at their bleeping patrol car.

"Hi, guys. My name is Dave Draper."

I forget how it went after that. The human being has a weird way of going numb and blocking things out — playing dead — when under siege.

Crazy, man. Why did we do the stuff we did? Don Howorth, Larry Scott, Zane, Yorton, Labra, McArdle, Zabo, Eifferman, Sipes. The money? No. Not the money. Sure, a few bucks would have paid some bills and broadened the smile, but no, not the dough.

The fame and glory? Such rewards circulated close to home and no one was profoundly impressed, least of all the champs. The brotherhood of recognition was quiet, almost silent. Fame and glory were as rewarding as the kiss of congratulations from the pretty girl in the miniskirt onstage. I'll never forget the authentic thunder of applause and cheering in New York, but those fans in those days were there for the same reasons we were.

It was the doing it that was good. And it's the doing it that continues to be good. None of us would change much if we were to do it all again. The smiles came when they weren't expected and they've lasted a long, long time.

Lift weights for fame, glory and money and you miss the point entirely.

If you don't understand what I'm saying, I can't explain it.

At last, for all my puffing and advice, I have one thing to say that is true:

Trust in the Lord with all your heart,
And lean not on your own understanding;
In all your ways acknowledge him,
And he will make your paths straight.

Proverbs 3:16, 17

Iron On My Mind is a compilation of Dave Draper's free weekly email newsletters, yours for the asking at his website, davedraper.com: — 1,500 words to accentuate, amplify and magnify your training experience. Sign up and you receive a weekly jolt of motivation accompanied by any variety of training information, nutritional recommendations, blasts from the past, or old, new, used or revised workout tips and hints. The conversational and insightful newsletter provides a welcome stimulus to keep your training spirit alive and well, and to keep you thinking and performing and growing.

Dave is the author of two motivating books on nutrition and weight training: *Brother Iron Sister Steel* — straight talk for bodybuilders — and *Your Body Revival* — straight talk for the overweight.

Dick Tyler is the author of *West Coast Bodybuilding Scene* and the medical reference text, *Alternative Chiropractic*.

These books are available at ontargetpublications.com.